Poetry Corner 2

A second collection of poems for children

BBC

Published by BBC Educational Publishing
Woodlands, 80 Wood Lane, London W12 0TT

First published 1993

ISBN 0 563 35389 9

Typeset by Goodfellow and Egan, Cambridge
Printed in England by Clays Ltd, St Ives plc

Contents

A few words...

Why poetry? What are poems anyway? - Simply one of the best ways of saying something.

I've heard it said by someone
It's been said
A poem's like a loaf of bread,

A necessary
Wholesome food,
Always fresh
And lasting good.

That's what John Mole says - you'll see some of his other poems too.

Well, in this collection you'll find many loaves: large ones, wholemeal ones, small ones and rolls - poems as fresh and good as new bread, in all shapes and sizes.

In schools all over the country children enjoy listening to them in the *Poetry Corner* programme on BBC School Radio. If you haven't heard this you could ask your teacher! And lastly, a big thank you once again to our team: to Jennifer Dunn, for her advice and help in choosing the poems, and to Ray and Corinne Burrows who drew all the pictures.

Colin Smith
Producer, *Poetry Corner*

Nearer the sky

I've been growing

Little by little, I've been growing,
It happened without me even knowing,
It happened so slowly without showing,
But today I *know* I've been growing.

For last year's coat which used to be roomy,
Today is tight and clinging to me,
It's short and it doesn't look right on the *new* me,
That's how I know I've been growing.

Daphne Lister

Growing

This pair of shoes
  is much too small,
they pinch and bother
  me.
I must have grown
  an inch or two.
Just take a rule
  and see.

I put my foot
  upon the board
and stretch my little
  toe.
What did you say —
  I've grown a size?
Of course.
  I told you so.

Jean Kenward

My friend Dee

My friend Dee
Is bigger than me,
And I'm more than three feet tall.
My friend Dee
Is bigger than me—
She can see over next-door's wall.

Whenever she looks over,
She laughs and giggles
Or runs and hides
And screams and shivers,
But she *never* tells me
What it is she can see...
Of course *I'm* not bothered at all.

Dave Ward

Friendly warning

LISTEN GRASS, TAKE
IT EASY. DON'T GROW
TOO TALL. THEY'LL JUST
BRING IN A LAWN
MOWER AND CUT
YOU DOWN SHORT.

SEE? I TOLD YOU THEY WOULD.

Robert Froman

Building a skyscraper

They're building a skyscraper
Near our street.
Its height will be nearly
One thousand feet.

It covers completely
A city block.
They've drilled its foundation
Through solid rock.

They made its framework
Of great steel beams
With riveted joints
And welded seams.

A swarm of workmen
Strain and strive
Like busy bees
In a honeyed hive

Building the skyscraper
Into the air
While crowds of people
Stand and stare....

James S. Tippett

The crane

Down by the station
there's a crane
fifty metres
high.
Its feet are square
upon the earth.
Its head is in
the sky,

And just a bit
below the top
a tiny, tiny
man
is wheeling everything
around...
but how do you think
he can?

Jean Kenward

City lights

Into the endless dark
The lights of the building shine,
Row upon twinkling row,
Line upon glistening line.
Up and up they mount
Till the tallest seems to be
The topmost taper set
On a towering Christmas tree.

Rachel Field

Climb the mountain

Climb
climb
the
mountain
high,
touch
the
clouds
and
see
the
sky.
Feel
the
wind
against
you
blow,
see
the
fields
far
far
below.

Wes Magee

Up in the air

Zooming across the sky,
Like a great bird you fly,
Aeroplane,
Silvery white
In the light.

Turning and twisting in air,
When shall I ever be there,
Aeroplane,
Piloting you
Far in the blue?

James S. Tippett

Higher and higher

I swing

I sit on my swing
And my feet let go
Backwards and forwards
To and fro
I make the air rush
As I swing by
I am a bird
I can fly
Over the trees
To the cloud in the sky
As I fall backwards
I lean on the air
And colours pass by
The higher I dare
From the blue in the sky
To the green of the grass
Backwards and forwards
Watch me pass
And the sunshine is bright
And the blackbird sings
And my swinging's forever
And ever
I swing

Elizabeth Lindsay

Helicopter

Helicopter
in the sky
where are you going
up so high?

Where are you going
in the blue?
Here I stand
and stare at you —

Here I stand
and wonder where
you are flying
through the air...

Helicopter,
answer me.
Where are you going?

Watch, and see!

Jean Kenward

The star

Twinkle, twinkle, little star,
How I wonder what you are!
Up above the world so high,
Like a diamond in the sky.

Traditional

Saturday night

On Saturday night I lost my wife
And where do you think I found her?
Up in the moon, singing a tune,
And all the stars around her.

Traditional

'Fourth floor!'

'Fourth floor!'
Is what I say
When I come in
From play.

My home
Is on that floor
It has a 'seven'
On the door.

Six other doors
Are on our hall
With a different family
Behind them all.

James S. Tippett

Seven old ladies

I heard somebody
somewhere say
seven old ladies
blew away,
seven old ladies
frail and thin:
the wind rushed out
and the wind rushed in
and one was seen
by all the people
sitting on top
of Salisbury steeple!

Two, I'm told,
went tossing, swirling
all the way
from Stowe to Stirling.
Three were caught
and counted, dancing
over the air
from Looe to Lancing.
But the smallest
shouted 'STOP!
Put me down
Before I drop!

North Wind, South Wind,
East or West —
don't you ruffle
my Sunday vest —
don't you touch me!
Don't you dare!
Blow the other ones
ANYwhere
But I certainly
will not stir....'
WHOOSH! Whatever
became of her?

Jean Kenward

Flying

I saw the moon,
One windy night,
Flying so fast —
All silvery white —
Over the sky
Like a toy balloon
Loose from its string —
A runaway moon.
The frosty stars
Went racing past,
Chasing her on
Ever so fast.
Then everyone said,
'It's the clouds that fly,
And the stars and moon
Stand still in the sky.'
But I don't mind —
I saw the moon
Sailing away
Like a toy
Balloon.

J. M. Westrup

The kites

Up in the air
See the kites fly,
Like coloured birds
In the wind-whipped sky.

I wish I were small
And light as air,
I would climb on a kite
And sail up there.

Then I'd drift upon
The paper wings
And hear the songs
That the wild wind sings.

What fun it would be
To look right down —
Over the park
And the rooftops of town.

The people below
Would stand and stare
And wish they were me
High, high in the air.

Daphne Lister

Giants and suchlike

Giant size

One Saturday morning
A Giant came by.
He was bigger than big
And higher than high.
His hands were enormous
And so were his feet,
And he caused quite a stir
As he walked down the street.

He frightened the ladies
Who'd gone out to shop,
And he caused all the hurrying
Traffic to stop.
He went to the market
And picked up a stall
Which was full of bananas
And gobbled them all.

But after a while
He went on his way
Leaving chaos behind him
And cries of dismay.
The giant was sorry
And said with a sigh,
'I can't help being big,
I can't help being high!'

Margaret Thomas

Giant Thunderclogs

Here comes Giant
  THUNDERCLOGS!
What a noise
  he makes!
How he rattles, rants
  and roars,
how he shouts
  and shakes!

Blundering
  across the hills
and stamping
  through the sky —
what a tantrum
  he is in
as he passes
  by!

Giant Thunderclogs
  is HUGE —
his mouth
  is like a pit
and all the echoes
  of the earth
come rushing out
  of it.

Not fifty thousand
  elephants
could trumpet
  such a din.
If you hear him
  at your gate —
DON'T
    LET HIM
        IN!

Jean Kenward

Who can tell?

How big is a dinosaur egg?
Bigger than a tennis ball,
smaller than a tree?
Taller than a turtle shell
But not as tall as me?
Who can see?

How hard is a dinosaur egg?
Harder than a chicken's
but not as hard as steel?
Tough enough to make you think
it isn't really real?
Who can feel?

What might hatch from a dinosaur egg?
Diplodocus, stegosaurus
with its spiny tail?
Allosaurus, brontosaurus
tapping at the shell?
Who can tell?

Judith Nicholls

A giant's so big

A giant's so big that he could stride
Across the world to the other side.

His legs are so long and strong that he
Could be back again in time for tea!

Daphne Lister

Giants

A giant is only a giant
To somebody very small.
And that's why I'll never
Ever be
Afraid of a giant
At all!

Irene Yates

Large and small

Think of a giant, then think of a mouse,
Think of a palace, then think of a house,
Think of an eagle, then think of a wren,
Think of a wrist watch, then think of Big Ben!

Daphne Lister

Beech leaves

In autumn down the beechwood path
  The leaves lie thick upon the ground.
It's there I love to kick my way
  And hear their crisp and crashing sound.

I am a giant, and my steps
  Echo and thunder through the sky.
How small the creatures of the woods
  Must quake and cower as I pass by!

This brave and merry noise I make
  In summer also when I stride
Down to the shining, pebbly sea
  And kick the frothing waves aside.

James Reeves

The giant visitor

Great big foot came
crashing through the ceiling,
stood heel to toe
on the settee;
great big stocking,
torn about the ankle,
great big leg,
a hairy knee.

Great big voice
came booming down the chimney;
'Yoo hoo!
Is anybody there?
It's dinner time,
I'm hungry,
so empty all your cupboards!
Cook a great big meal;

GIVE ME A SHARE!'

Irene Rawnsley

Giant

A Giant
is someone
ten miles high
whose feet
touch the ground
and whose head
hits the sky.

And if I
saw a Giant
walking down
our way
I wouldn't stop
But I'd run away
and hide in a doorway
quiet as a fly...

And I wouldn't come out
till he'd gone by.

Ivy O. Eastwick

Don't call alligator long-mouth till you cross river

Call alligator long-mouth
call alligator saw-mouth
call alligator pushy-mouth
call alligator scissors-mouth
call alligator raggedy-mouth
call alligator bumpy-bum
call alligator all dem rude word
but better wait
till you cross river

John Agard

Said a long crocodile

Said a very l–o–n–g crocodile,
'My length is a terrible trial!
I know I should diet
But each time I try it
I'm hungry for more than a mile!'

Lilian Moore

Playground pleasures

School's up!

Down in the playground
It's a freeze up, sneeze up
Waiting for the bell.
Then off into line
Where it's a squeeze up, tease up
No more shout and yell.
But very soon
It's a knees up, wheeze up
P.E. in the hall.
Followed by a
Cheese up, please up
Dinner time call.
Then afternoon and
Busy bees up, seize up
When all work's done.
Until it's
Ease up, tea's up
So it's home time.........RUN!

Ian Souter

In the playground

In the playground
Some run round
Chasing a ball
Or chasing each other;
Some pretend to be
Someone on TV;
Some walk
And talk,
Some stand
On their hands
Against the wall
And some do nothing at all.

Stanley Cook

Georgie Porgie

Georgie Porgie, pudding and pie,
Kissed the girls and made them cry;
When the boys came out to play,
Georgie Porgie ran away.

Traditional

Why?

Why do we have to have boys around?
We don't like what they do.
When they are out in the open ground
they scuffle, and tumble too.

They're not content to listen and dream.
They don't want to read or write.
They're dirty and noisy and out of hand,
and asking for a fight.

Why do we have to have boys around?
It's nicer on our own.
We're older in all our ways than them —
we don't mind being alone.

There are kinds of being and kinds of seeing
they never can understand.
I don't want a boy to my birthday tea.
I just want a Disco band.

Jean Kenward

Johnny

Johnny's a terrible boaster.
He's big, and he's strong
and he's tough.
He struts and he swanks
in the playground.
He likes to be noisy
and rough.

When Johnny's at home he is different.
I know, because
somebody said
he's frightened of darkness,
and always
he takes his old teddy
to bed.

Jean Kenward

Just when

It's always the same.
Just when you're playing a game,
Just when it's exciting
And interesting
With everyone racing
And chasing,
Just when you're having so much fun,
Somebody always wants something done!

Max Fatchen

Friends

As friends we
whisper,
discuss,
argue,
then float messages across
  crowded playgrounds
that only we know
  and understand.

As friends we
walk,
stumble,
run,
then sprint after each other,
so close we exchange shadows
  as we go.

As friends we
laugh,
cry,
care,
taste each other's thoughts
and share each other's moods.

One girl, one boy,
one friendship to enjoy.
One lock, one key,
that's you and me!

Ian Souter

Daft as a brush

Simple Simon

Simple Simon met a pieman
Going to the fair;
Says Simple Simon to the pieman,
Let me taste your ware.

Says the pieman to Simple Simon,
Show me first your penny;
Says Simple Simon to the pieman,
Indeed I have not any.

Simple Simon went a-fishing,
For to catch a whale;
All the water he had got
Was in his mother's pail.

He went to catch a dickey bird,
And thought he could not fail;
Because he'd got a little salt,
To put upon its tail.

Traditional

The walrus

The walrus is not pretty,
He would make an awkward pet.
If you took him to bed to cuddle
Your pyjamas would get wet.

Finola Akister

There was a lady loved a swine

There was a lady loved a swine,
Honey, quoth she,
Pig-hog, wilt thou be mine?
Hoogh, quoth he.

I'll build thee a silver sty,
Honey, quoth she,
And in it thou shalt lie.
Hoogh, quoth he.

Pinned with a silver pin,
Honey, quoth she,
That you may go out and in.
Hoogh, quoth he.

Wilt thou have me now,
Honey? quoth she.
Speak or my heart will break.
Hoogh, quoth he.

Traditional

Night starvation or The biter bit

At night my Uncle Rufus
(Or so I've heard it said)
Would put his teeth into a glass
Of water by his bed.

At three o'clock one morning
He woke up with a cough,
And as he reached out for his teeth —
They bit his hand right off.

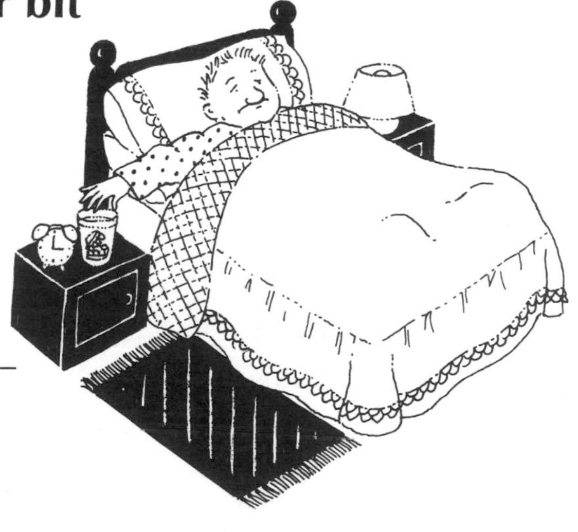

Carey Blyton

Fingummy

Fingummy's fat
And Fingummy's small,
And Fingummy lives
With the boots in the hall.

If Fingummy bites,
If Fingummy tears,
If Fingummy chases you
Up the stairs

Shout 'Bumble-Bee Soup
And Bluebottle Jam.'
And run up to bed

can
you
as
fast
as

Cos Fingummy lives
Where there's never no light
And Fingummy makes
The dark sounds of the night,
And Fingummy's fat
And Fingummy's small
And Fingummy lives
In the dark, in the hall.

Mike Harding

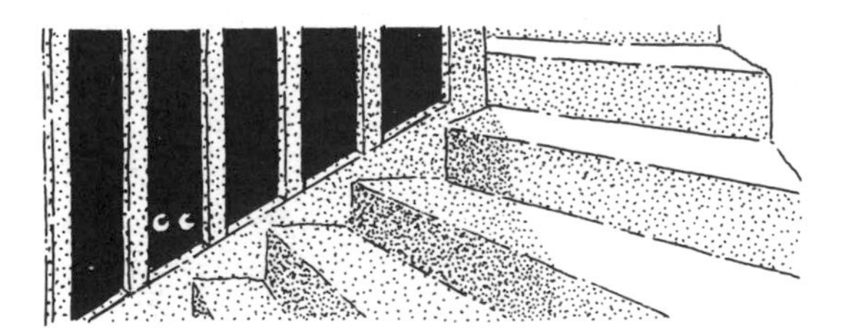

A catapillow

A catapillow
is a useful pet

To keep
upon your bed

Each night you simply
fluff him up

Then rest
your weary head.

Roger McGough

Algy

Algy met a bear,
A bear met Algy.
The bear was bulgy,
The bulge was Algy.

Anonymous

Ever see a shark?

Ever see
a shark
picnic
in the park?

If he offers
you a bun

run.

Roger McGough

Sing a song of science

Sing a song of science,
A rocket-full of mirth;
Four-and-twenty monkeys
Orbiting the earth.

When the rocket landed,
It came down on the moon,
And there they scoffed the Gruyère cheese
With knife and fork and spoon.

Carey Blyton

The octopus

The octopus has lots of legs
That grow out at all angles.
One day he tried to cross them
And they finished up all tangles.

Finola Akister

Not a hippopotamus

The old grey hippopotamus
Can't understand the likes of us,
He baths himself in pools of mud
Because it's cooling to his blood.
But as for us we know we ought to
Have our baths in clean hot water.
So please don't cry and make a fuss
When mother puts you in the suds:
Remember that you're one of us,
And not a hippopotamus.

A. Depledge

The American Elk

The American Elk — also known as the wapiti —
Runs through the maple woods, clippety-cloppety,
Favoured with feet of remarkable property
Wapitis never have need of chiropody.

Dick King-Smith

What am I?

Tears

I cried today.
My face was strangely wet,
And tears ran down
for anyone
to see.

I stuck my tongue out
just a tiny bit
and swallowed them.
They tasted
just like me.

Jean Kenward

Susannah

Susannah put her apron on,
'I'm a witch, I'm a witch,' she said,
'And if you don't give me some diamonds,
I'll magic you into brown bread.
Who am I?' she asked her teddy.
'You're a witch,' her teddy bear said.

Susannah put her slippers on,
'I'm a queen, I'm a queen,' she said,
'And if you don't give me some rubies,
I'll chop all the curls off your head.
Who am I?' she asked her teddy.
'You're a queen,' her teddy bear said.

Susannah put her nightdress on,
'I'm so tired, so tired,' she said.
Then she yawned and took out her ribbons
And snuggled down into her bed.
'Who am I?' she asked her teddy.
'Susannah,' her teddy bear said.

Richard Edwards

Noses

I looked in the mirror
and looked at my nose:
it's the funniest thing,
the way it grows
stuck right out where all of it shows
with two little holes where the breathing goes.

I looked in the mirror
and saw in there
the end of my chin
and the start of my hair
and between there isn't much space to spare
with my nose, like a handle, sticking there.

If ever you want
to giggle and shout
and can't think of what
to do it about,
just look in the mirror and then, no doubt,
you'll see how funny YOUR nose sticks out!

Aileen Fisher

Mirror friends

When we look in the mirror,
Me and my friend,
I am brown and she is white.
When we look in the mirror,
Me and my friend,
My hair is dark and hers is light.

And my eyes are black as a raven's wing,
And hers are as blue as a sapphire ring.
She likes chips
And I like rice,
She likes ketchup
And I like spice.

But when we look in the mirror,
Me and my friend
We feel we are the same as same can be,
Though I am brown and she is white,
We could be sisters,
She and me.

Jamila Gavin

Shapes

A snake is slim and sinuous,
he's sleek and smooth and slick.
He slides upon his journeys
like an oily sort of stick.
He's secret, and he's certain that
he knows where he is going.
He's like a piece of water that is
flowing flowing flowing....

A rabbit, though, is rather fat:
he's beautifully rounded.
He flicks his tail fearfully
when any noise is sounded.
He's fluffy and he's frightened
as he nibbles at the grasses
and dashes to a hiding place
when anybody passes.

And are YOU fat, or are you thin?
Have you a hole to hide in?
A friend to go to parties with?
Something on wheels to ride in?
And are you round, or are you square,
or are you fitted nicely
with lines and angles everywhere?

What is YOUR shape, precisely?

Jean Kenward

If I wasn't me

If I wasn't me,
I'd rather be
Batman or (second choice)
Robin.

I'd come to school
In the Batmobile
Friends in the back,
Me at the wheel.

The teacher would say,
'Batman?'
And I'd say, 'Here, Miss.'

If I wasn't me,
I'd rather be
Wonderwoman's daughter.

I'd wear a cloak
With fancy shorts,
And win every race
In the school sports.

The teacher would say
'Thanks, Wondergirl!'
And mum would win
the Mothers' Race.

Allan Ahlberg

Hair, Hair

Haircut (1)

Snip, snap, snickle-snackle,
just a little more!
Curls and swirls and tufty bits
scatter on the floor!

Snip, snap, snickle-snackle,
won't my friends all stare!
Dare I, dare I, DARE I look?
Is my head quite BARE?

Snip, snap, snickle-snackle,
I don't think I dare!
Shall I, shan't I open eyes?
Is there NOTHING there?

Judith Nicholls

Haircut (2)

I hate having my hair cut;
And when it's done,
I hate going to school next day
And being *told* about it —
By everyone.

'Oh, you've had your hair cut,' they say.
'Oh, you should wear a hat!'
'Oh, you've had a *bare*-cut,' they say.
And silly things like that.

I can stand having my hair cut,
Though I'd rather let it grow.
What I can't stand
Is being *told* I've had it cut —
As if I didn't know!

Allan Ahlberg

Soft spot

'No, don't look round.
You'll not feel a thing.'
So I shut my eyes
and started to sing.
But then the pain —
Oh, what a disaster
as nurse peeled back
the sticking plaster.
Now Grandad and I
have something in common:
a little bald patch —
but mine's on my bottom.

John C. Desmond

Song

Brown hair, black hair,
auburn, ginger, fair.
Short hair, long hair,
curled, waved, straight.
Silver for the old man,
for the dame, grey.
None for the little baby
born yesterday.

John C. Desmond

If I had shiny scissors

If I had shiny scissors
And I owned a barber's shop,
I'd snip all day till five and even then
I wouldn't stop,
I'd walk home trimming hedges
And lawns and dogs and cats,
And woe betide all grans who passed
With feathers in their hats!

Richard Edwards

Hooray for hair

What's your favourite colour hair?
Hands up, who say yellow!
Hands up, who say brown!
Hands up, who say black ... and red ...
Now put your hands back down.
Now, hands up
who say ... tangerine!
And who say pink! and limey green!
What colour is your teacher's hair?
Is it dark or is it fair?
Whatever colour it may be,
Let's shout ... HOORAY FOR HAIR!

Clive Riche

Granny Granny please comb my hair

Granny Granny
please comb my hair
you always take your time
you always take such care

You put me to sit on a cushion
between your knees
you rub a little coconut oil
parting gentle as a breeze

Mummy Mummy
she's always in a hurry-hurry
rush
she pulls my hair
sometimes she tugs

But Granny
you have all the time in the world
and when you're finished
you always turn my head and say
'Now who's a nice girl?'

Grace Nichols

The top and the tip

Hair is the top of a person,
a chimney's the top of a house,
a cover's the top of a book,
the tail is the tip of a mouse.

The sky is the top of the world,
the top of the sky is space,
a flower's the top of a stem,
the nose is the tip of the face.

Charlotte Zolotow

Fuzzy Wuzzy was a bear

Fuzzy Wuzzy was a bear,
    A bear was Fuzzy Wuzzy,
When Fuzzy Wuzzy lost his hair
    He wasn't Fuzzy, was he?

Traditional (USA)

On the outside

The furry ones

I like —
the furry ones —
the waggy ones
the purry ones
the hoppy ones
that hurry,

The glossy ones
the saucy ones
the sleepy ones
the leapy ones
the mousy ones
that scurry,

The snuggly ones
the huggly ones
the never, never
ugly ones ...
all soft
and warm
and furry.

Aileen Fisher

Yakkity Yak

Yakkity Yak was a shaggy old yak
Who lived in high Tibet.
He truly was the hairiest yak
That you have ever met.
He had hair from his toes
To the tip of his nose,
So his toes never froze
In the wintery snows.
He had hair where hair
Never usually grows,
Had Yakkity Yak.

Herbert Kretzmer

Furry bear

If I were a bear,
And a big bear too,
I shouldn't much care
If it froze or snew;
I shouldn't much mind
If it snowed or friz —
I'd be all fur-lined
With a coat like his!
For I'd have fur boots and a brown fur wrap,
And brown fur knickers and a big fur cap.
I'd have a fur muffle-ruff to cover my jaws,
And brown fur mittens on my big brown paws.
With a big brown furry-down up to my head,
I'd sleep all the winter in a big fur bed.

A.A. Milne

Look at your hat!

Look at your hat!
Just look at your hat!
It's back to front
And squashed quite flat.
Look at your hat!

Look at your shirt!
Just look at your shirt!
It's inside out
And black with dirt.
Look at your shirt!

Look at your dress
Just look at your dress!
It's rumpled and crumpled
And needs a press.
Look at your dress!

Look at your shoes!
Just look at your shoes!
They're full of holes —
Not fit to use.
Look at your shoes!

Look at your face!
Just look at your face!
It hasn't been washed.
What a disgrace!
Look at your face!

GO HOME

Barbara Ireson

Stripey tiger

A tiger has stripes
From its head to its tail,
A polar bear hasn't,
Nor has a whale.

A panda is patchy,
A leopard has spots,
A giraffe's sort of blotchy,
A deer has white dots.

An elephant's grey
And a fox is all red,
But a tiger has stripes
From his tail to his head.

Daphne Lister

New clothes and old

I rather like New Clothes
They make me feel so fine,
Yet I am not quite Me,
The Clothes are not quite mine.

I really love Old Clothes,
they make me feel so free,
I know that they are mine,
For I feel just like Me.

Eleanor Farjeon

Christmas party

The children's carol

Here we come again, again, and here we come again!
Christmas is a single pearl swinging on a chain,
Christmas is a single flower in a barren wood,
Christmas is a single sail on the salty flood,
Christmas is a single star in the empty sky,
Christmas is a single song sung for charity.
Here we come again, again, to sing to you again,
Give a single penny that we may not sing in vain.

Eleanor Farjeon

Christmas

My goodness, my goodness,
It's Christmas again.
The bells are all ringing.
I do not know when
I've been so excited.
The tree is all fixed,
The candles are lighted,
The pudding is mixed.

The wreath's on the door
And the carols are sung,
The presents are wrapped
And the holly is hung.
The turkey is sitting
All safe in its pan,
And I am behaving
As calm as I can.

Marchette Chute

Ten white snowmen

Ten white snowmen standing in a line,
One toppled over, then there were nine.

Nine white snowmen standing up straight,
One lost his balance, then there were eight.

Eight white snowmen in a snowy heaven,
The wind blew one over, then there were seven.

Seven white snowmen with pipes made of sticks,
One slumped to the ground, then there were six.

Six white snowmen standing by the drive,
One got knocked down, then there were five.

Five white snowmen outside the front door,
An icicle fell on one, then there were four.

Four white snowmen standing by the tree,
One slipped and fell apart, then there were three.

Three white snowmen underneath the yew,
One crumbled overnight, then there were two.

Two white snowmen standing in the sun,
One melted right down, then there was one.

One white snowman standing all alone,
Vanished without a trace, then there were none.

John Foster

Holly

A little bit of holly
Is always very jolly
At the top of a Christmas tree;
And the sight of any berry
Who would not agree is very
Enjoyable for anyone to see?
But it's also very certain,
As I think you will agree,
The brightest bit of holly
Is *anything* but jolly
... when the silly thing
is
sticking into ME!

John Tompkins

At Christmas

We have a candle
in our house,
and when the Christmas
night is come
its light upon
the window ledge
brings every traveller
home.

So it was
many years ago ...
And now, beyond
the darkening trees
we watch the stars
come riding up
from their huge
distances:

Look — one among them
seems more bright
than all the sky
from East to West!
It hangs above
the Holy Child,
and is
at rest.

Jean Kenward

If I could be a pilot

If I could be a pilot
Each Christmas Eve I'd fly
To fetch a fluffy snow cloud
From the distant Arctic sky,
I'd chase it, catch it, tow it home
And tie it to a tree,
So snow would fall on Christmas Day
On all my friends and me.

Richard Edwards

Warmest greetings

It's Christmas morning
And we've planned
To leave our footprints
In the sand;
To picnic barbecue once more,
And eat our luncheon by the shore.
The presents from our Christmas tree
We'll open up, beside the sea.
Relaxing in the scorching sun,
We'll play some party games, then run
To cool off in the water clear —
We get a suntan *every* year!

Here, winter snows are out of reach —
We're Christmassing on BONDI BEACH!

Trevor Harvey

What's in the parcel?

Lift it, sniff it,
rattle, shake!
Is it heavy?
Will it break?

Tear the corner,
listen, look!
Scooter? Computer?
Adventure book?

Can I bend it, throw it,
spend it, lick it?
Will it fly?
Or could I kick it?

Will it work outside?
In rain?
A skateboard? Bike?
Electric train?
Here we go...
 Oh, NO!
  not SOCKS AGAIN!

Judith Nicholls

Bang! Crash! Wallop!

Watch out!

Watch out!
Here comes my friend
Vapinder!
Vapinder makes a lot of noise
He's one of those noisy kind of boys
He doesn't talk, he always screeches —
Wherever you are, his shouting reaches!
Take my tip —
As Vapinder nears —
STICK YOUR FINGERS
IN YOUR

\\ //
— EARS!!! —
// \\

Irene Yates

Street at night

Not a sound came from the street
Just some silently stepping feet
Going farther and farther
Growing fainter and fainter
Till they had gone in the distance
And could be heard no more.

Thomas Young

Balloon

I blew a balloon,
It grew bigger and bigger,
And bigger,
Till it filled the room.
No one could get in,
Until my brother —
A pin, through the keyhole he poked it and . . .
BOOM!

I blew a balloon,
In front of the cat.
It rose up,
On claw and on fang.
I said 'Nothing to fear,
A balloon, look, here . . . here!'
But she spat and she clawed at it . . .
BANG!

I blew a balloon,
In the classroom at break,
Then I hid it under my shirt.
The teachers said 'Sonny,
Let go of your tummy.'
So I did, and the balloon went . . .
PHUUUURRRRRTTT!

Clive Riche

Sound of fire

The sound of fire is:
A hiss,
A sputter,
A crackle,
A flutter,
A lick,
A rumble,
A roar,
A grumble,
A cry,
A pop,
A shift,
A flop,
A race,
A sweep,
A spit,
A leap,
A whoosh,
A boom,
A snap,
A plume,
A cackle,
A crash,
A fall
Of ash . . .

Mary O'Neill

Jazz-Man

Crash and
CLANG!
Bash and
BANG!
And up in the road the Jazz-Man sprang!
The One-Man-Jazz-Band playing in the street,
Drums with his Elbows, Cymbals with his Feet,
Pipes with his Mouth, Accordion with his Hand,
Playing all his Instruments to Beat the Band!
TOOT and
Tingle!
HOOT and
Jingle!
Oh, what a Clatter! How the tunes all mingle!
Twenty Children couldn't make as much Noise *as*
The Howling Pandemonium of the One-Man-Jazz!

Eleanor Farjeon

The sound collector

A stranger called this morning
Dressed all in black and grey
Put every sound into a bag
And carried them away

The whistling of the kettle
The turning of the lock
The purring of the kitten
The ticking of the clock

The popping of the toaster
The crunching of the flakes
When you spread the marmalade
The scraping noise it makes

The hissing of the frying-pan
The ticking of the grill
The bubbling of the bathtub
As it starts to fill

The drumming of the raindrops
On the window-pane
When you do the washing-up
The gurgle of the drain

The crying of the baby
The squeaking of the chair
The swishing of the curtain
The creaking of the stair

A stranger called this morning
He didn't leave his name
Left us only silence
Life will never be the same.

Roger McGough

The pines

Hear the rumble,
Oh, hear the crash.
The great trees tumble.
The strong boughs smash.

Men with saws
Are cutting the pines —
That marched like soldiers
In straight green lines.

Seventy years
Have made them tall.
It takes ten minutes
To make them fall.

And breaking free
With never a care,
The pine cones leap
Through the clear, bright air.

Margaret Mahy

Field and forest

The foal

There's something new in the meadow:
it's soft, and brown and small
but its legs are long and straggly,
it can hardly stand at all.

The grey mare, gently breathing
there, in the lush, wet green,
has a new-born foal beside her
as limp as plasticine.

He rose, as we stopped to wonder,
and wobbled a little bit,
as if he were lately come to the world
and wasn't too sure of it.

Then he turned, and touched his mother,
searching her drowsed and dim
for the warm, sweet milk she carried.
What name shall we give to him?

Jean Kenward

The song of a mole

All I did this afternoon was
Dig, dig, dig,
And all I'll do tomorrow will be
Dig, dig, dig,
And yesterday from dusk till dawn
I dug, dug, dug.
I sometimes think I'd rather be
A slug, slug, slug.

Richard Edwards

Listen

Down in the forest
something stirred
by the light
of the silver moon.
Was it an owl
or was it a fox?
It was only
a small teaspoon.

John C. Desmond

In the woods

There are badgers in the woods
and nightingales.
Or so they say.
Foxes have made their dark, safe hide-outs there.
Not far away
Country mice scamper, quickly looking for
something to eat:
berries, or nuts, or acorns
for a special
and secret treat.

There are shadows in the woods
and sighing things
I never see.
A fallen twig might crackle suddenly
under a tree,
or a shy rabbit run to hide its brown
and bob-tailed self.
I wouldn't be surprised at anything...
even an elf.

Jean Kenward

A forest by night

When the sun goes down
And the bats come out
and the shadowy badger
Is moving about,

Then I sometimes hide
In my favourite tree
And watch all the creatures
Who can't see me:

The deer on the paths,
The mice in the leaves,
The foxes that tiptoe
As quietly as thieves.

A forest by night
Is an eerie place
Where a hole in the treetops
Can look like a face . . . .

Richard Edwards

Badgers

Badgers come creeping from dark under ground,
Badgers scratch hard with a bristly sound,
Badgers go nosing around.

Badgers have whiskers and black and white faces,
Badger cubs scramble and scrap and run races,
Badgers like overgrown places.

Badgers don't jump when a vixen screams,
Badgers drink quietly from moonshiny streams,
Badgers dig holes in our dreams.

Badgers are working while you and I sleep,
Pushing their tunnels down twisting and steep,
Badgers have secrets to keep.

Richard Edwards

Midnight visitors

Hedgehog comes snuffing
in his prickly coat,
scuffing the leaves for slugs.

Cat comes soft as a moth,
a shadow painted on the lawn
by moonlight.

Owl comes floating,
sits still as a cat on the wall,
watching, listening.

Mouse freezes under the leaves
on tiptoe paws,
quick eyes pin-bright,
hungry.

Irene Rawnsley

The lake monster

In the deep dark forest
Is a deep dark lake.
In the deep dark water
Lurks a long, dark snake.

Or is it a dragon?
Or some kind of whale?
No one knows exactly
But it's got a long, long tail.

Moving through the water
It twists in loops and lumps.
It's got a strange-shaped head
With bulging eyes and bumps.

It doesn't surface often,
Which is really just as well,
For some think it's unlucky —
Strange are the tales they tell.

And those who see it tremble,
Those who see it quake,
The long dark creature
In the deep dark lake.

Daphne Lister

All my relations

Family album

I wish I liked Aunt Leonora
When she draws in her breath with a hiss
And with fingers of ice and a grip like a vice
She gives me a walloping kiss.

I wish I loved Uncle Nathaniel
(The one with the teeth and the snore).
He's really a pain when he tells me *again*
About what he did in the War. . . .

I wish I loved Hetty and Harry
(Aunt Hilary's horrible twins)
As they lie in their cots giving off lots and lots
Of gurgles and gargles and grins . . . .

If we only could choose our relations
How happy, I'm certain, we'd be!
And just one thing more: I am perfectly sure
Mine all feel the same about me.

Charles Causley

Be nice to a new baby

Be nice to a new baby,
I know it's not much fun:
She doesn't joke, won't play games,
And cannot even run.

She occupies your mother,
Who could be doing things
Like cutting out, or sticking down,
Or pushing you on swings.

Be kind to a new baby,
It might pay off in the end —
For that naggy little bundle
Could turn out to be a friend.

Fay Maschler

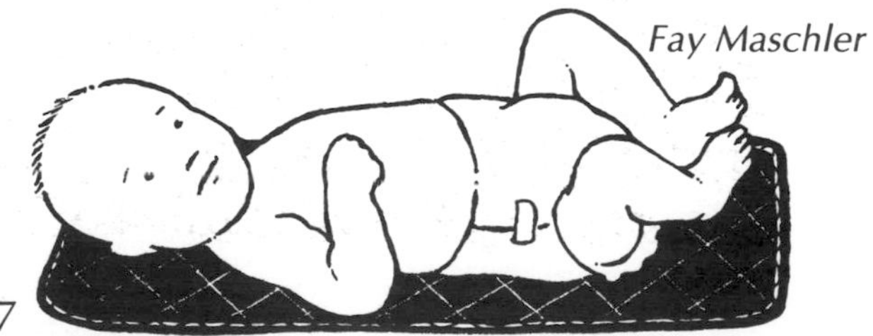

Music makers

My auntie plays the piccolo,
My uncle plays the flute,
They practise every night at ten,
Tweetly tweet *Toot-toot*!

My granny plays the banjo,
My grandad plays the drum,
They practise every night at nine,
Plankety plank *Bumm-bumm*!!

My sister plays the tuba,
My brother plays guitar,
They practise every night at six,
Twankity *Oom-pa-pa*!!!

My mother plays the mouth organ,
My daddy plays oboe,
They practise every night at eight,
Pompity-pom suck-blow!!!!

Spike Milligan

The tree down the street

The tree down the street
has little green apples
that never get bigger
never turn red.
They just drop on the ground
get worm holes
brown spots.
They're
just right for stepping on
like walking on bumpy marbles,
or green eggs that break with a snap
just right for gathering
in a heap behind the hedge
waiting
for a target.
Here comes my brother.

Diane Dawber

Great Grandad

Great Grandad is
Grandad's Dad.
He doesn't go to work
But stays at home
And sits in his armchair
Every day.
He looks at the garden
And nods his head.
Now then, he says.
Nod, nod, nod.
Tell me what you've done at school
Today —
And he cocks his head on one side
Like a sparrow
To listen
And his eyes twinkle.
Well done, he says.
Nod, nod, nod.
Well done.

One day, Great Grandad will probably be
A hundred years old.

Irene Yates

My sister Laura

My sister Laura's bigger than me
And lifts me up quite easily.
I can't lift her, I've tried and tried;
She must have something heavy inside.

Spike Milligan

Old and friendly

Grandfather gruffit

When Grandfather's snoozing
Each day, after tea,
He snores and he snorts
And he quite frightens me!

When I see his head drooping
And his old eyelids close,
I get ready for the grunts that
He makes through his nose.

Then he growls like a tiger
And groans like a bear,
He's not like an old man
Asleep in a chair.

If I tickle his feet
He gruffits with rage,
Like an angry old lion
Being teased in a cage!

The strange thing is this,
When he opens his eyes,
He's not cross— or noisy—
And looks in surprise.

For he doesn't know
That he gruffits and snores,
Like a grumpy old tiger
With thorns in its paws!

Daphne Lister

Auntie Betty

slip slop
slip slop

that's the sound
my Auntie Betty makes
in her big baggy slippers

slip slop
slip slop

she never goes
outside the house

they say
it's agora-something

but I always call
on my way to school

she's a brilliant cook
and she laughs a lot

I like my Auntie Betty
even if
she's not so good to look at

slip slop
slip slop

Joan Poulson

Like Grandad

Grandad's dog has short
fat legs.
Like Grandad.
His eyes are sharp and
brown and bright.
Like Grandad.
When he's asleep he
snores and snorts.
Like Grandad.
He loves me and
I love him.
Like Grandad.

Joan Poulson

There was an old man

There was an old man
Had a face made of cake,
He stuck it with currants
And put it in to bake.

The oven was hot,
He baked it too much,
It came out covered
With a crunchy crust.

The eyes went pop,
The currants went bang,
And that was the end
Of that old man.

James Kirkup

There was an old woman

There was an old woman of Chester-le-Street
Who chased a policeman all over his beat.

She shattered his helmet and tattered his clothes
And knocked his new spectacles clean off his nose.

'I'm afraid,' said the Judge, 'I must make it quite clear
You can't get away with that sort of thing here.'

'I can and I will,' the old woman she said,
'And I don't give a fig for your water and bread.

I don't give a hoot for your cold prison cell,
And your bolts and your bars and your handcuffs as well.

I've never been one to do just as I'm bid.
You can put me in jail for a year!'

So they did.

Charles Causley

Fears and fancies

What's that?

What's that rustling at the window?
Only the curtain flapping in the breeze.

What's that groaning in the garden?
Only the branches swaying in the trees.

What's that rattling at the front door?
Only the wind in the letter-box flap.

What's that drumming in the bathroom?
Only the dripping of the leaking tap.

What's that hissing in the front room?
Only the gas as it burns in the fire.

What's that murmur in the kitchen?
Only the whirring of the tumble drier.

What's that shadow lurking
in the corner beside the door?
It's only your clothes where you left them
lying on the bedroom floor.

John Foster

You never know

Things may happen.
You never know.
Butter may fall
Instead of snow. . . .

Olive Dove

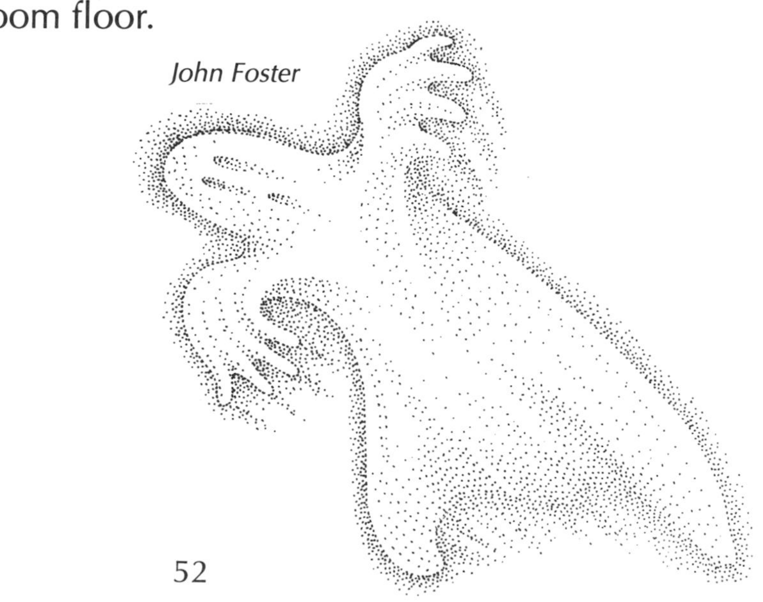

The night visitor

Some
THING
went
bump
in the
night.

THUMP
in the
night.
Gave
me a
fright.

A shadow
moved
on the
wall.
Long-
legged
and
terribly
tall.

A ghoulie?
Or
ghostie
in white?
A trick
of the
light?

No,
Nothing
went
bump
but that
BEASTLY

lump
of a
cat
Asleep
On my
bed.

She
made me
jump
last night.

Ann Bonner

Countdown

There are ten ghosts in the pantry,
There are nine upon the stairs,
There are eight ghosts in the attic,
There are seven on the chairs,
There are six within the kitchen,
There are five along the hall,
There are four upon the ceiling,
There are three upon the wall,
There are two ghosts on the carpet,
Doing things that ghosts will do,
There is one ghost right behind me
Who is oh so quiet . . . BOO.

Jack Prelutsky

Children's delight

If all the rain was chocolate rain,
We shouldn't say: 'Wish it was fine again!'
We should want to go out in the wettest weather
And sweep all the chocolate drops together.

Anonymous

Beardful

There was an Old Man with a beard,
Who said, 'It is just as I feared!
   Two Owls and a Hen,
   Four Larks and a Wren,
Have all built their nests in my beard!'

Edward Lear

Being alone

Every morning after register
Miss says 'Up you jump!
Off to assembly! Into line!
Hold somebody else's hand!'
But nobody holds mine.

When we go off to do PE
We run around the hall
Then Miss calls 'Everybody stand!
Find yourself a partner!'
But nobody takes my hand.

I try to pretend
That I don't care —
I haven't ever cried.
But somebody has
Very quietly, quietly,
Right deep down,
Inside.

Irene Yates

Who?

I'm sure it wasn't me who spoke
When I was shinning up the oak,
So who, as I climbed up that tree,
Said: 'Get those nasty feet off me!'

Richard Edwards

Little Miss Tuckett

Little Miss Tuckett
Sat on a bucket,
Eating some peaches and cream;
There came a grasshopper
And tried hard to stop her;
But she said,'Go away, or I'll scream.'

Anonymous

I'm really quite glad

I'm really quite glad,
That I'm not made of wool,
For if it should rain
When I go to school,
What would my friends
And acquaintances think,
If all of a sudden
I started to shrink?

Helen Russell

High days and holidays

The roundabout

Round and round the roundabout
Down the Slippery Stair —
I'm always to be found about
When circus men are there.
The music of the roundabout,
The voices in the air,
The horses as they pound about,
The boys who shout and stare —
There's such a lovely sound about
A circus or a fair.

Clive Sansom

The merry-go-round

Up and down
They swoop,
The fairground horses galloping nose to tail
To a blaring tune.

My horse is green
With a blue mane
And a scarlet saddle.
I hang on tight to a golden pole,
Lean over and call into his ear

'Go faster horse! Go higher, higher!'
Soon we are spinning and swooping together
My green and blue and scarlet horse
And I
Clutched tight to a golden pole.

Jessica James

The caterpillar fair

Ten little caterpillars
wriggled to the fair.
What did they do
when they got there?

One ate potatoes,
one ate pie,
one bought a telescope
to look at the sky.

One blew a trumpet,
one played guitar,
two sat together
in a dodgem car.

One met an elephant,
one saw a seal
and one went riding
on the whirly whirly wheel!

Irene Rawnsley

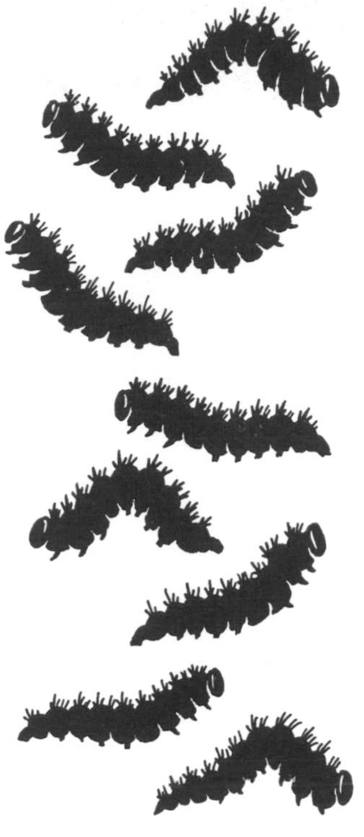

Sack race

Toes in,
knees in.
Quick now,
squeeze in!
Itchy back,
tickle-knees,
hairy sack
makes you sneeze.
Two-feet-hop,
never stop!
Snap, snip,
don't trip . . .
There and back
jumping sack . . .
One . . .
two . . .
three . . .
OFF!

Judith Nicholls

Bouncy castle

We bounced on the bouncy castle
and I jumped really high.
My sister stayed close to the edge
where Mum could keep an eye.
'Now just be careful,' Mum said.
as I bounced up high again,
and that was when the tip of my chin
met the knee of my best friend Ben!

Brian Moses

On the beach

Gull
Full
Fishing cull

Smack
Tack
Bladderwrack

Sun
Fun
Sticky bun

Tide
Slide
Donkey ride

Soak
Joke
Can of coke

Cool
Pool
Seaside school

Sand
Band
Wonderland

Munch
Lunch
Mr Punch

John C. Desmond

At the Zoo

There are lions and roaring tigers, and enormous camels and things,
There are biffalo-buffalo-bisons, and a great bear with wings,
There's a sort of a tiny potamus, and a tiny nosserus too —
But *I* gave buns to the elephant when *I* went down to the Zoo!

There are badgers and bidgers and bodgers, and a Superintendent's House,
There are masses of goats and a Polar, and different kinds of mouse,
And I think there's a sort of a something which is called a wallabaloo —
But *I* gave buns to the elephant when *I* went down to the Zoo!

If you try to talk to the bison, he never quite understands;
You can't shake hands with a mingo — he doesn't like shaking hands.
And lions and roaring tigers hate saying, 'How do you do?' —
But *I* give buns to the elephant when *I* go down to the Zoo!

A. A. Milne

Imagination

I built a castle
on the sand.
The tide came in
and wrecked it.

I built a castle
on the rocks.
The frost crept in
and cracked it.

I built a castle
in the air.
The birds flew in
and loved it.

Castles built
among the clouds
are those that poems
are made of.

John C. Desmond

No tears at bedtime

Night lights

There is no need to light a night-light
On a light night like tonight;
For a night-light's light's a slight light
When the moonlight's white and bright.

Anonymous

Silverly

Silverly,
Silverly,
Over the
Trees
The moon drifts
By on a
Runaway
Breeze.

Dozily,
Dozily,
Deep in her
Bed,
A little girl
Dreams with the
Moon in her
Head.

Dennis Lee

After a bath

After my bath
I try, try, try
to wipe myself
till I'm dry, dry, dry.

Hands to wipe
and fingers and toes
and two wet legs
and a shiny nose.

Just think how much
less time I'd take
if I were a dog
and could shake, shake, shake.

Aileen Fisher

You don't frighten me!

When I get frightened,
I stack,
I pack,
I pile,
I file
All my teddies around my bed.
And like soldiers at attention,
They offer me a wall of protection.
Then I skip into bed,
Squeeze under my duvet
And whisper,
'Come on darkness,
You big, black, bullying, bubble of trouble.
I'm ready with my teddies,
YOU DON'T FRIGHTEN ME!'

Ian Souter

Late-night caller

The tick of the clock,
the click of the lock,
a shoeless sock
on the stair,

the groan of the floor,
the squeak of a door,
the sigh of a drawer —
who's there?

A current of air,
a pencil of light —
'I'm back, son. All right?
Goodnight!'

Sue Cowling

Goodnight

When I climb into bed and snuggle up tight,
I know that I'll want to say goodnight
to hippo, to seal and to polar bear,
to the fluffy dog that I won at the fair,
to the photo of dad in the frame by my bed,
to my monkey, my mouse and my one-eyed ted,
to my old elephant with a tear in its tum,
and an extra special goodnight to my Mum!

Brian Moses

Shiver and sweat

August afternoon

Where shall we go?
  What shall we play?
What shall we do
  On a hot summer day?

We'll sit in the swing.
  Go low. Go high.
And drink lemonade
  Till the glass is dry.

One straw for you,
  One straw for me,
In the cool green shade
  Of the walnut tree.

Marion Edey

Today was really hot...

Today was really hot,
so I tried to keep myself cool.
I dropped a pile of ice cubes
into the paddling pool.
Mum chased me with the hosepipe
and caught me in its spray,
then accidentally soaked our cat
who quickly ran away.

I drank a long cold drink
and ate the biggest lolly.
I sat around in the shade,
underneath dad's old brolly.
I read my favourite book,
it was far too hot to play,
'It's sure to rain next week,' Mum said,
'When we start our holiday!'

Brian Moses

Somersaults

It's fun turning somersaults
and bouncing on the bed,
I walk on my hands
and I stand on my head.

I swing like a monkey
and I tumble and I shake,
I stretch and I bend,
but I never, never break.

I wiggle like a worm
and I wriggle like an eel,
I hop like a rabbit
and I flop like a seal.

I leap like a frog
and I jump like a flea,
there must be a rubber
inside of me.

Jack Prelutsky

Sore throat

'I have a very sore throat', said Jemima,
'And I'm in so much terrible pain,
My voice has gone scratchy and squeaky,
Will I ever get better again?'
'It will take a long time,' said her doctor,
'It's a thing at which no one should laugh,
It's the worst sort of germ you could possibly have,
As you happen to be a giraffe.'

Finola Akister

Mary had a little lamb (1)

Mary had a little lamb
Its fleece was white as snow,
And everywhere that Mary went
That lamb was sure to go.

Traditional

Mary had a little lamb (2)

Mary had a little lamb
Its fleece she went and sold.
Now she has a woolly jumper,
But the lamb is feeling cold.

Finola Akister

There was a baby kangaroo

There was a baby kangaroo
With very little else to do
But clamber up into his mother's pouch.

Mrs Kangaroo cried 'Ouch'
Because, of course, it must be told,
Although she loved her baby
His feet were very cold.

Finola Akister

Snow!

For years and years
I waited for snow,
drove my family mad
just wanting to know,
will it snow this year,
will this year be the one?

But now it's come
I just want it to go,
my fingers are frozen
and so are my toes.
There's an icicle formed
at the tip of my nose.
My ears disappeared
half an hour ago.
It's not like I thought:
how I hate this snow!

Brian Moses

Phew!

Trickle, trickle drops of sweat.
Can this be why I am wet
From my forehead to my toes
and some drops drip from my nose?
Could it be the sun's too hot
or the curry from the pot?
Trickle, trickle drops of sweat.
Maybe I should see the vet.

John C. Desmond

The chestnut stall

As I remember it
Everything that day was white or black or red.
The snow was everywhere
And still fell down.

The man at the chestnut stall was there as usual
In a black coat, his nose a cherry red,
Stamping his great black boots
Against the frozen path.

My scarf and gloves were red,
My shoes were black.
I saw that we made a pattern together,
The man and I in the snow.

Beside the stall stood an iron stove
Criss-crossed with iron bands.
Inside the stove live coals glowed spitting red
And on a shovel laid upon the coals
Fat roasted chestnuts burst their blackened shells.

He put some in a bag for me.
'Take care! Don't burn yourself!', he said.

I remember that day
With its pattern of white and black and red
And the hot chestnuts held in a paper bag
Against my icy fingers.

Jessica James

Mr Nobody

I know a funny little man,
As quiet as a mouse,
Who does the mischief that is done
In everybody's house!
There's no one ever sees his face,
And yet we all agree
That every plate we break was cracked
By Mr Nobody.

'Tis he who always tears our books,
Who leaves the door ajar,
He pulls the buttons from our shirts,
And scatters pins afar;
That squeaking door will always speak,
For, prithee, don't you see,
We leave the oiling to be done
By Mr Nobody....

The fingermarks upon the door
By none of us are made;
We never leave the blinds unclosed,
To let the curtains fade.
The ink we never spill; the boots
That lying round you see
Are not our boots — they all belong
To Mr Nobody.

Anonymous

Goblin

There's a goblin
in the cupboard
underneath the stairs.

I can hear him
snuffling, snorting,
shifting his affairs....

Sometimes, I have
seen his shadow
crouched behind a boot,

Twisty, dark,
and like a bit of
muddy turnip root.

People say
the cupboard's empty:
there is nothing there

But a pile
of bags and boxes.
I could show you where

There's a goblin
bowing, bending
in the flaky dark.

If you turn
the handle gently
you may hear him....

Hark!

Jean Kenward

The Shadow Man

At night-time
As I climb the stair
I tell myself
There's nobody there.

But what if there is?
What if he's there —
The Shadow Man
At the top of the stair?

What if he's lurking
There in the gloom
Of the landing
Right outside my room?

The Shadow Man
Who's so hard to see
What if he's up there
Waiting for me?

At night-time
As I climb the stair
I tell myself
There's nobody there.

John Foster

It wasn't me

Dad, you know that broken glass
Lying on the kitchen floor?
The one that's in a puddle,
Right there by the door?

Well, it wasn't me that did it.

Mum, you know my little brother,
The one who tells those lies?
The one who always blames me
When he's hurt himself and cries?

Well, it wasn't me that did it.

Dad, you know those new school shoes,
The ones that were so tough?
The ones that really cost a lot?
They weren't quite tough enough.

But it wasn't me that did it.

Mum, you know that little jug
Our dad's mum gave to you?
The one that's on the dresser?
Well, now it's cracked in two.

But it wasn't me that did it.

Dad, you know that broken glass
Lying on the kitchen floor?
The one that's in a puddle,
Right there by the door?

Well...that's right, how did you know?
It wasn't me that did it (honest!).

Tony Bradman

Who did it?

Well, it wasn't me
'cos I wasn't here
and I can prove it
without any fear.
I wasn't in London
or Birmingham
so I must have been
elsewhere.
If that was so
I couldn't be here.
Whoever it was
I didn't see.
As far as I know
it was nobody.

John C. Desmond

The man who wasn't there

As I was going up the stair
I met a man who wasn't there.
He wasn't there again today —
Oh, how I wish he'd go away!

Anonymous

Some one

Some one came knocking
   At my wee, small door;
Some one came knocking,
   I'm sure — sure — sure;
I listened, I opened,
   I looked to left and right,
But naught there was a-stirring
   In the still dark night;
Only the busy beetle
   Tap-tapping in the wall,
Only from the forest
   The screech-owl's call,
Only the cricket whistling
   While the dewdrops fall,
So I know not who came knocking,
   At all, at all, at all.

Walter de la Mare

No answer

There was an Old Man who said, 'Well!
Will *nobody* answer this bell?
   I have pulled day and night,
   Till my hair has grown white,
But nobody answers this bell!'

Edward Lear

Who lives here?

The snake

I don't think
I'd like to touch
a slippery, slimy
grass snake much,
sliding, slithering
through the green. . .
gone, as soon as
partly seen.

Do you believe
a grass snake knows
where he comes from
and where he goes?
Does he guess
when he looks at me
that I'm a *person* —
or just a tree?

Jean Kenward

Only in my opinion

Is a caterpillar ticklish?
Well, it's always my belief
That he giggles, as he wiggles
Across a hairy leaf.

Monica Shannon

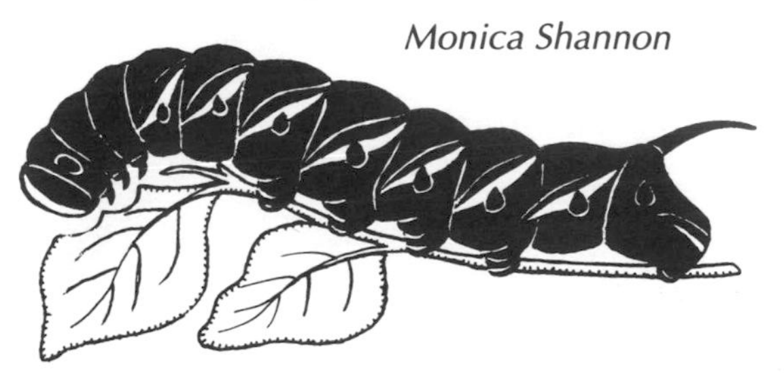

Littlemouse

Light of day going,
Harvest moon glowing,
People beginning to snore,
Tawny owl calling,
Dead of night falling,
Littlemouse opening her door.

Scrabbling and tripping,
Sliding and slipping,
Over the ruts of the plough,
Under the field gate,
Mustn't arrive late,
Littlemouse hurrying now.

Into a clearing,
All the birds cheering,
Woodpecker blowing a horn,
Nightingale fluting,
Blackbird toot-tooting,
Littlemouse dancing till dawn.

Soon comes the morning,
No time for yawning,
Home again Littlemouse creeps,
Over the furrow,
Back to her burrow,
Into bed. Littlemouse sleeps.

Richard Edwards

Grandpa Tortoise

Grandpa Tortoise —
He's so slow. . .
Do you ever think
he'll EVER go?
Grandpa Tortoise
can't decide
whether it
is nice outside,
or, if it
is nicer IN.
He just thinks
he may begin
moving. . .moving
carefully
over to
the apple tree. . .

When he's thought
a little. . .when
he has thought
that thought again. . .
maybe he
will move a bit —
(when he's sort of
thought of
it).

Jean Kenward

Can you guess?

It's got a little twitchy, twitchy nose —
but it's not a rabbit.
It's got a little sniffy, sniffy nose —
but it's not a dog.
It's got four tiny scratchy, scratchy paws —
but it's not a kitten.
It's got nibbly, nibbly, nibbly teeth —
but it's not a hamster.
It's got a wiggly, wriggly, squiggly tail
And wiggly ears
And glittery eyes
And the field is its world
And a hole is its house —
can you guess?

It's a mouse! Sssshhh. . .

Irene Yates

Slugs

Slugs, slugs
Crawl through the grass,
Watching all the beetles
As they scurry past.

Slugs, slugs
Crawl so slow,
Leaving tracks of silver
Wherever they go.

Slugs, slugs
Crawl all along the wall,
Popping little horns out,
Make no sound at all.

John Kitching

The radio men

When I was little more than six
I thought that men must be
Alive inside the radio
To act in plays, or simply blow
Trumpets, or sing to me.

I never got a glimpse of them,
They were so very small.
But I imagined them in there,
Their voices bursting on the air
Through that thin, wooden wall.

Elizabeth Jennings

Who's in

'The door is shut fast
And everyone's out.'
But people don't know
What they're talking about!
Says the fly on the wall,
And the flame on the coals
And the dog on his rug
And the mice in their holes,
And the kitten curled up,
And the spiders that spin —
'What, everyone's out?
Why, everyone's in!'

Elizabeth Fleming

Houses

Where would you live if you were me?
A lonely lighthouse in the sea
With a garden of waves and rocks?
A narrowboat nosing through locks?
A windmill with a winding stair
And round rooms stacked like building blocks —
Would you live there?

Where would I live if I were you?
A wooden ark, a floating zoo.
A swaying eyrie in a tree
Would do for me.
An igloo with an icy dome,
A painted gypsy caravan,
A paper palace in Japan
Could be my home.

Sue Cowling

Good company

I sleep in a room at the top of the house
With a flea, and a fly, and a soft-
  scratching mouse,
And a spider that hangs by a thread
  from the ceiling,
Who gives me each day such a curious
  feeling
When I watch him at work on his
  beautiful weave
Of his web that's so fine I can hardly
  believe
It won't all end up in such terrible tangles,
For he sways as he weaves, and spins as
  he dangles.
I cannot get up to that spider, I know,
And hope he won't get down to me here
  below,
And yet when I wake in the chill
  morning air
I'd miss him if he were not still swinging
  there,
For I have in my room such good
  company,
There's him, and the mouse, and the fly, and the flea.

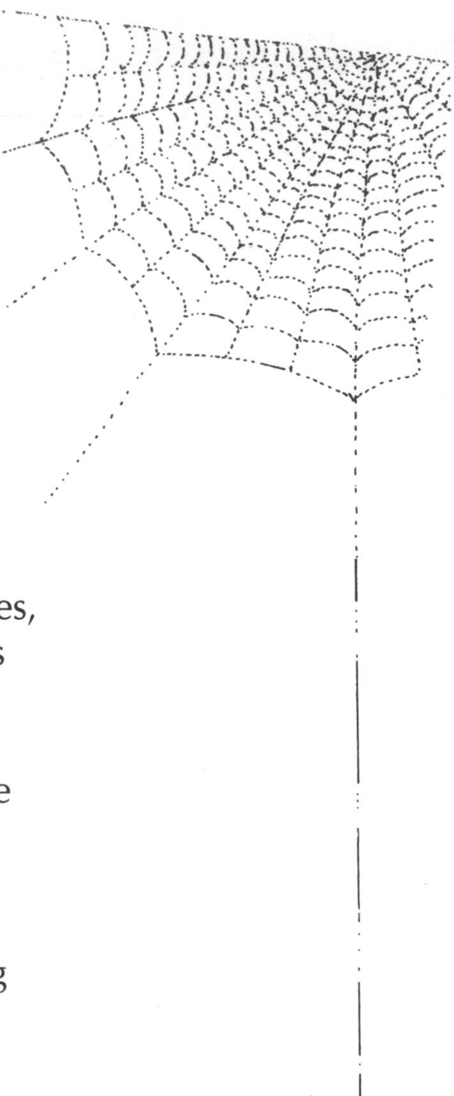

Leonard Clark

Everybody's somebody

Inside

There are lots of things
They won't let me do —
I'm not big enough yet
They say.
So I quietly wait
Till I'm all grown up
And I'll show them all,
One day.
I could show them now
If they gave me the chance
There are things I could do
If I tried.
But nobody knows,
No nobody knows, that I'm
Really a giant
Inside.

Irene Yates

The three unlucky men

Near Wookey Hole in days gone by
  Lived three unlucky men.
The first fell down a Treacle Mine
  And never stirred again.

The second had no better fate
  And he too is no more.
He fell into a Custard Lake
  And could not get to shore.

The third poor fellow, sad to say,
  He had no fairer luck,
For he climbed up a Porridge Hill
  And half-way down got stuck.

Alas, alas! man is but grass,
  Let life be short or long;
And all the birds cried 'Fancy that!'
  To hear this merry song.

James Reeves

Tall Paul

When I was small, they'd smile and say:
'Don't worry, Paul, that's just the way
You're built; you'll grow up tall one day.'

But now I'm grown and *seven feet* tall,
They smile and say: 'Don't worry, Paul,
Er. . .have you thought of basketball?'

Richard Edwards

Sunlight or surprise?

No, don't go near him, people say,
He's full of fleas, so keep away
From Old Jack Rags.

He's never tidy, never clean,
The filthiest tramp you've ever seen,
Is Old Jack Rags.

He lives on rubbish, sleeps in dirt,
He's only got one grubby shirt,
Has Old Jack Rags.

His teeth are black, his eyes are red,
He eats small children with his bread,
Does Old Jack Rags.

No, don't go near him, people say,
But I went near, just yesterday,
To Old Jack Rags

And: 'Do you sleep in dirt?' I said,
'And eat small children with your bread?
Well, Old Jack Rags?'

Then was it sunlight or surprise
That made those tears start from the eyes
Of Old Jack Rags?

Richard Edwards

Deborah Delora

Deborah Delora, she liked a bit of fun —
She went to the baker's and she bought a penny bun;
Dipped the bun in treacle and threw it at her teacher —
Deborah Delora! what a wicked creature!

Traditional

Man in the Moon

Does the Man in the Moon make music
as he sits up there alone
as bright as silver paper
and smooth as a pumice stone?

Does he sing to himself, as he travels
the great, wide, star-pricked sky?
Or whistle a tune like a blackbird
as he goes sailing by?

Does the Man in the Moon feel lonely,
or does he like to be there —
as pale as milk in the morning,
and gold, in the cold night air?

Jean Kenward

Scarecrow independence

I may look raggy and queer
— but I bow to no man.

My face may look silly and sad
— but I'm no snowman.

I may stand stiff and still
— but hold my head high.

I raise my old hat to no one
— not even when *you* walk by.

James Kirkup

The classroom circle of friends

and I like Anne
Dan likes me ➔ I like Anne
Dee likes Dan Anne likes John
Titch likes Dee John likes Mike
Mo likes Titch Mike likes Ron
Mitch likes Mo Ron likes Paul
Ray likes Mitch Paul likes Pam
Bert likes Ray Pam likes Jack
George likes Bert Jack likes Sam
Gert likes George Sam likes Jane
Jock likes Gert Jane likes Rick
Faye likes Jock Rick likes Jo
Chris likes Faye Jo likes Mick
May likes Chris Mick likes Val
Ken likes May Val likes Jill
Phil likes Ken Jill likes Trish
Trish likes Phil

(➔ start here)

Wes Magee

The lion and the unicorn

The lion and the unicorn
Were fighting for the crown;
The lion beat the unicorn
All around the town.

Some gave them white bread,
And some gave them brown;
Some gave them plum cake
And drummed them out of town.

Traditional

Oh, no...!

A tale of woe!

Oh, the clock's stopped ticking,
And the door keeps sticking,
And the donkey's started kicking
Down the stable doors.

We haven't any money
And the weather isn't sunny
And the wallpaper's all honey
From the baby's sticky paws!

Daphne Lister

Old Mother Hubbard

Old Mother Hubbard
Went to the cupboard,
To fetch her poor dog a bone;
But when she got there
The cupboard was bare
And so the poor dog had none.

Traditional

When Old Mother Hubbard

When Old Mother Hubbard
Went to the cupboard
Her dog for a morsel would beg.
'Not a scrap can be found,'
She explained to her hound —
So he bit the poor dear on the leg.

Max Fatchen

Alas! Alas! for Miss Mackay!

Alas! Alas! for Miss Mackay!
Her knives and forks have run away;
And when the cups and spoons are going,
She's sure there is no way of knowing.

Anonymous

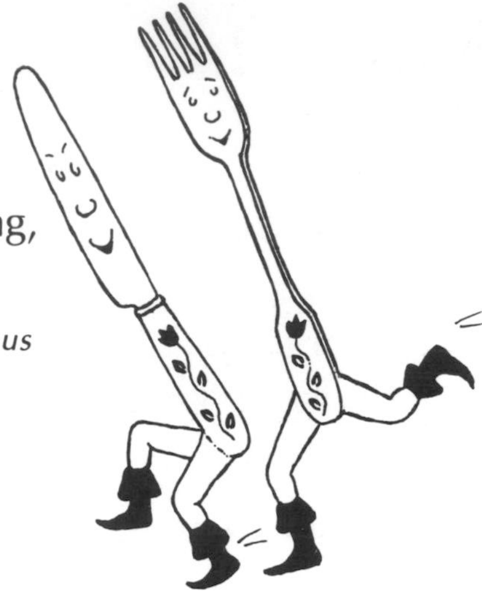

Jack and Jill

Jack and Jill
Went up the hill,
To fetch a pail of water;
Jack fell down,
And broke his crown,
And Jill came tumbling after.

Then up Jack got,
And home did trot,
As fast as he could caper;
He went to bed
To mend his head
With vinegar and brown paper.

Traditional

Waiting

When is he coming?
Will he be long?
I still cannot see him,
I hope nothing's wrong.
Perhaps he's got lost.
Perhaps you should phone.
I've been watching for hours
Here on my own.
He might have forgotten
He's coming to stay.
Are you sure he'll remember
That today is the day?

Michelle Magorian

Intruders

What's nice is
when I'm left
to my own devices.

Getting on with things
in my own quiet way
or doing simply nothing,
not a thing all day.

But people have to interfere:
'Stop that! Do this!
No, not in here!' And all
for the sake of something to say.

Grown-up intruders.
When I grow up I hope
I'm not as rude as they.

Roger McGough

The quarrel

I'm never going round to her place again,
And I won't have her coming here to play.
She hates all my games and I hate her.
I don't want to see her today.

She pulled my hair, I kicked her leg,
She pushed me and gave me this bite.
Those teeth marks are hers. Look at my arm!
It's her fault we had a big fight.

She'd better say sorry, she'd better.
I am not saying sorry to her.
I'll play by myself and if she comes near
I'll pretend I'm a tiger and go grrruh!

Michelle Magorian

Octopus

Once upon a big red bus
I sat next to an octopus.
O what a fidget and a fuss
Made that wriggly octopus!

His eight arms waved and waved about
Until I really had to shout.
'Why ever don't you move away?'
I heard a bearded old man say.

The reason was that in each arm
The funny thing held gifts to charm
A boy or girl — a ball, a rope,
A watch, a brass toy telescope.

I won't tell you any more
But let you guess the other four.
He shuffled off at the next stop
With a flippety, flappity, fluppety flop.

All of his eight gifts did he
Carry with him carefully. . .
And I was sad because, you see,
He hadn't given one to me.

Olive Dove

All wet

Tears on Monday

Two white shirts on the washing line
Were flapping high and drying,
When on the clothes peg next to them
A small sock started crying;

And as its tears splashed to the ground
Like rain drops, pitter-patter,
A shirt said: 'Why the weepies, sock?
Whatever is the matter?'

'I'm sorry,' sniffed the sock, looking
From one shirt to the other,
'But how would you feel if the wind
Had carried off your brother?'

Richard Edwards

Waiting for the first drop

No-one knows the exact moment
of what hour
the first drop of rain will fall.

But after one whole week
of blinding sun
of scorched grass
of wilting leaves,
it somehow seems important.

So I watch and wait
along with the birds,
along with the ants,
along with every living
breathing thing,

for that first heavy
cool splash of rain
to wet the page
of this poem about the rain.

Raymond Souster

There was a young lady of Spain

There was a young lady of Spain,
Who couldn't go out in the rain,
  For she'd lent her umbrella
  To Queen Isabella,
Who never returned it again.

Anonymous

Shower

fierce
spring
rain
full
gushing
drain
grey
puddled
street
wellies
for
feet

drab
steely
sky
umbrellas
held
high
children
want
out
harassed
mothers
shout

cars
make
spray
birds
huddle
away
cats
lie
asleep
plants
drink
deep

rain
becomes
drops
slows
and
stops
doors
open
wide
people
step
outside

Moira Andrew

My uncle's umbrella

Under my uncle's umbrella
Are Uncle Augustus and I.
My uncle's quite fat —
If it wasn't for that,
I'd manage to keep myself dry.

Colin West

Who spoke?

Who spoke?
'Croak! Croak!
We spoke,
Frogs from the pond,
The still, cool pond,
That we've leaped beyond.

And now that the sun has set
And the sky's dark as jet
We are deep in grass made wet

By cool washes and sloshes of rain,
Rivers and slivers of rain,
Buckets of bountiful rain.

What bliss to be
So moist and so free.
We croak continually.'

Olive Dove

Wet

It's wet, wet, wet,
And my mackintosh is dripping,
Wet, wet, wet,
And my wellingtons are slipping,
Wet, wet, wet,
And the wind is fiercely whipping
Through the trees.

Wet, wet, wet,
Heavy hail-stones are dropping,
Wet, wet, wet,
On our heads and all the shopping,
Wet, wet, wet,
Sending muddy puddles hopping,
Wet, wet, wet,
Up to my knees.

Michelle Magorian

Albert Arthur Algernon

Albert Arthur Algernon
wouldn't put his wellies on.
When it rained
his feet got wet.
Then the snow —
not found him yet.
Not a trace of Algy, none.

John C. Desmond

Rainy nights

I like the town on rainy nights
  When everything is wet —
When all the town has magic lights
  And streets of shining jet!

When all the rain about the town
  Is like a looking-glass,
And all the lights are upside-down
  Below me as I pass.

In all the pools are velvet skies,
  And down the dazzling street
A fairy city gleams and lies
  In beauty at my feet.

Irene Thompson

Everything's wet

Everything's wet
  in the woods today,
hung with a silver
  chain.
All night long
  came the slushing sound
of calling
    falling
      rain.

I heard it as
  I went to sleep.
I heard it when I fell
  into a dreamful
nothingness —
  and when I woke,
    as well.

Everything's washed
  and glimmering
with water
  on its skin.
I walked through the woods
  with my wellies on
splashing in green
  on green.
The birds, they sang
    as if they drank
water
    in every song.
Everything's wet
    in the woods today —
and that's where I
    belong.

Jean Kenward

Going on a train

The child in the train

The train stands still
  And the world runs by.
Yonder runs a tree
  And a cloud in the sky.
Here flies a pony
  On the running road,
And there flows the quickest
  River ever flowed.

The mountains on the edge
  Roll away like the tide,
The backs of the houses
  Pass on a slide,
The little farms slip off
  As soon as one looks,
And the little churches vanish
  With their spires and their rooks.

The buttercup embankments,
  The telegraph wires,
The names of the stations,
  The small heath fires,
The hoardings in the fields,
  And the people in the street,
Go whizzing into somewhere
  While I keep my seat.

The little cities trot,
  And the little hamlets trip,
The meadow with its cow,
  The sea with its ship,
The forest and the factory,
  The hedge and the hill —
The world goes running by
  While the train stands still!

Eleanor Farjeon

To a fat lady seen from the train

O why do you walk through the fields in gloves,
  Missing so much and so much?
O fat white woman whom nobody loves,
Why do you walk through the fields in gloves,
When the grass is soft as the breast of doves
  And shivering-sweet to the touch?
O why do you walk through the fields in gloves,
  Missing so much and so much.

Frances Cornford

Waving at trains

Down in the dandelion field,
Watching the holiday trains go by,
All afternoon we waited,
Billy and I.

Train after train after train – –
There were twenty at least, we reckoned;
But hardly a head turned round, and no one gave
The answering wave;
And we gradually lost all hope,
And our hands slackened.

Just one more train. . .

It came, slowly climbing the slope:
On cushiony seats the holiday-people sat;
They read their books, and chatted and ate;
The train swept by, solemn and grand.
Then, at the very last,
(The train was almost past),
Suddenly, there at the window, a face leaned out – –
And look! a smile, a wave, a fluttering hand!

Till that train was out of sight,
We waved, Billy and I did – –
We waved with all our might.

John Walsh

A peanut sat on the railroad track

A peanut sat on the railroad track,
His heart was all a-flutter;
Along came a train — the 9.15 —
Toot, toot, peanut butter!

Anonymous

Song of the train

Clickety-clack,
Wheels on the track,
This is the way
They begin the attack:
Click-ety-clack,
Click-ety-clack,
Clickety-*clackety*,
Click-ety
Clack.

Clickety-clack,
Over the crack,
Faster and faster
The song of the track:
Clickety-clack,
Clickety-clack,
Clickety-clackety,
Clackety
Clack.

Riding in front,
Riding in back,
Everyone hears
The song of the track:
Clickety-clack,
Clickety-clack,
Clickety-*clickety*
Clackety
Clack.

David McCord

A young lady of Spain

There was a young lady of Spain
Who was dreadfully sick on a train,
Not once, but again
And again and again,
And again and again and again.

Anonymous

Night train

The train
is a shiny caterpillar
in clackity boots
nosing through the blind night,
munching mile after mile
of darkness.

Irene Rawnsley

Up with the lark

The cock doth crow

The cock doth crow
To let you know
If you be wise
'Tis time to rise:
For early to bed,
And early to rise,
Is the way to be healthy
And wealthy and wise.

Traditional

The alarm

All night long
 the little red clock
  makes not a single
   sound;

Silently
 it works away
  sending the two hands
   round

Until it gives
 a kind of click
  and bursts into
   a shout —

'Time to get up!'
 calls the little red clock.
  'Time to be up,
   and out!'

Jean Kenward

Sunday morning

Warm bed,
Big yawn,
Breakfast cooking,
Mum calls.

Getting dressed,
Darren, singing
Out of tune,
Sun at window,
Fluffy clouds,
Milkman clinking,
Church bells ringing,
'Come on! Eat up!
We don't want to be late!'
But we always are!

Brian Morse

Waking up

Oh! I have just had such a lovely dream!
And then I woke,
And all the dream went out like kettle-steam,
Or chimney-smoke.

My dream was all about — how funny, though!
I've only just
Dreamed it, and now it has begun to blow
Away like dust.

In it I went — no! in my dream I had —
No, that's not it!
I can't remember, oh, it is *too* bad,
My dream a bit.

But I saw something beautiful, I'm sure —
Then someone spoke,
And then I didn't see it any more,
Because I woke.

Eleanor Farjeon

Somewhere Town

Which is the way to Somewhere Town?
  Oh, up in the morning early;
Over the tiles and the chimney-pots,
  That is the way, quite clearly.

And which is the door to Somewhere
    Town?
  Oh, up in the morning early;
The round red sun is the door to go
    through,
  That is the way, quite clearly.

Kate Greenaway

Elsie Marley

Elsie Marley is grown so fine,
She won't get up to feed the swine,
But lies in bed till eight or nine,
  Lazy Elsie Marley.

Traditional

What a wonderful day!

Days may come, and days may go,
Some bring rain; and some bring snow.
Some bring laughter, some bring tears;
They turn to weeks, then months, then
  years.
Some bring birthdays, presents and
  smiles,
On some we travel miles and miles
To holiday places in the sun,
Where there is sea, and sand, and fun.
Some days are spooky, like Halloween,
And some are the best you've ever seen.
Carnival, Christmas, a day at the zoo. . .
Special for someone, special for *you*.
These are the times when you just want
  to say:
Oh, what a wonderful, *wonderful* day!

Tony Bradman

On the beach

Driving to the beach

On the road
smell fumes and tar
through the windows
of the car.

But at the beach
smell suntan lotion
and wind
  and sun
      and ocean!

Joanna Cole

Until I saw the sea

Until I saw the sea
I did not know
that wind
could wrinkle water so.

I never knew
that sun
could splinter a whole sea of blue.

Nor
did I know before
a sea breathes in and out
upon a shore.

Lilian Moore

The sea's treasures

In swept the sea
With a swirl and a swish,
It shimmered and whispered,
'Choose what you wish.'

And the sea showed its treasures
At the edge of the shore,
Shining bright pebbles
And shells by the score.

Long ribbons of seaweed
That shone gold and red,
'I'll share them, I'll share,'
The sea softly said.

Daphne Lister

Seaside

Come — O do come
  quickly
down to the beach
  with me
before a foot
  has broken it!
Green, green
  the sea,
but the sand
  is golden
listening
  to the tide
with wet weed
  and white shells
    and bits of wood beside. . .

The waves are small
    and distant,
but look, they're coming
    near,
and soon they'll reach
    the castle
and the moat we've scrabbled
    here.
Dig, dig
    your fastest!
Build, build
    a wall —
after the water's
    touched it, there'll be
      nothing left at all.

Jean Kenward

Yesterday our family visited the seashore!

Yesterday our family visited the seashore
To search for sea creatures and a whole lot more.
But all we found were
A squashed-up drink can,
A plastic toy made in Japan,
A length of fishing line,
A punctured football, just like mine,
A soggy cigarette packet,
A smashed-up old tennis racket,
A child's yellow beach shoe,
A screwed-up dirty tissue,
A coil of rusty wire,
A black rubber car tyre ,
A piece of food in kitchen foil,
And a rockpool full of thick filthy oil.
All this in one morning on the seashore,
A whole lot of pollution and not much more!

Ian Souter

Paddling

Now the water is over my toes,
and now it is up to my knees,
here where the quick tide flows
and feet and fingers freeze;
the spray kissing my face,
it is a desperate race
between tide and me,
between land and sea.

Half of me in water, half in air,
half of me wet, half dry,
but I meet the waves four square
with the weed swimming by,
and safe as an anchor I stand,
then splash to the land,
to the welcoming coast,
and warm as toast.

Leonard Clark

Greedy gulls

Wheeling and circling
The sea gulls fly.
They sail on the wind
In the stormy sky.
Their wings are as grey
As the misty sea,
And they hover, waiting,
Waiting for me.

They follow me, calling,
They want to be fed,
For they know that I have
In my pocket some bread.
When I take out the bag
They descend in a cloud
All flapping and fluttering
And screeching aloud.

Swooping and screaming
They dive to the ground
Squabbling and fighting
For what they have found.
In a very short time
They have picked the place clean,
And there isn't a solitary
Crumb to be seen.

Margaret Thomas

At the seaside

When I was down beside the sea
A wooden spade they gave to
me
To dig the sandy shore.

My holes were empty like a cup.
In every hole the sea came up,
Till it could come no more.

Robert Louis Stevenson

Sand

Sand in your fingernails
Sand between your toes
Sand in your earholes
Sand up your nose!

Sand in your sandwiches
Sand on your bananas
Sand in your bed at night
Sand in your pyjamas!

Sand in your sandals
Sand in your hair
Sand in your trousers
Sand everywhere!

John Foster

Jellyfish

Jellyfish,
jellyfish,
floats along and slaps you on the belly
fish.

Just when you thought you'd go for a swim,
just when you thought it was safe to go in.

Jellyfish,
jellyfish,
saw one in a programme on the telly
fish.

Thinking about it kept me awake,
I just don't think that I can take

Jellyfish,
jellyfish,
trod on one at Margate with Aunt Nelly
fish

If you see one in the sea then give me a shout,
catch it in a bucket but keep your fingers out.

Jellyfish,
jellyfish,
odd and funny-looking umbrelly
fish,
slimy old seaside smelly
fish,

Jellyfish,
jellyfish,
jellyfish,
jellyfish.

Brian Moses

Who'd want *that* for a pet?

The animal picture book

I opened my picture book,
turned to page one;
a cheeky brown monkey
jumped into the room.

I opened my picture book,
turned to page two;
a bright yellow parrot
said 'How do you do?'

I opened my picture book,
turned to page three;
a nimble grey mouse
scampered onto my knee.

Now we all live together
in one little house,
me and my monkey,
my parrot and mouse.

Irene Rawnsley

Bear in there

There's a Polar Bear
In our Frigidaire —
He likes it 'cause it's cold in there.
With his seat in the meat
And his face in the fish
And his big hairy paws
In the butter dish,
He's nibbling the noodles,
He's munching the rice,
He's slurping the soda,
He's licking the ice.
And he lets out a roar
If you open the door.
And it gives me a scare
To know he's in there —
That Polary Bear
In our Fridgitydaire.

Shel Silverstein

Maggie

There was a small maiden named Maggie,
Whose dog was enormous and shaggy;
The front end of him
Looked vicious and grim —
But the tail end was friendly and waggy.

Anonymous

Eletelephony

Once there was an elephant,
Who tried to use the telephant —
No! No! I mean an elephone
Who tried to use the telephone —
(Dear me! I am not certain quite
That even now I've got it right.)

Howe'er it was, he got his trunk
Entangled in the telephunk;
The more he tried to get it free,
The louder buzzed the telephee —
(I fear I'd better drop the song
Of elephop and telephong!)

Laura E. Richards

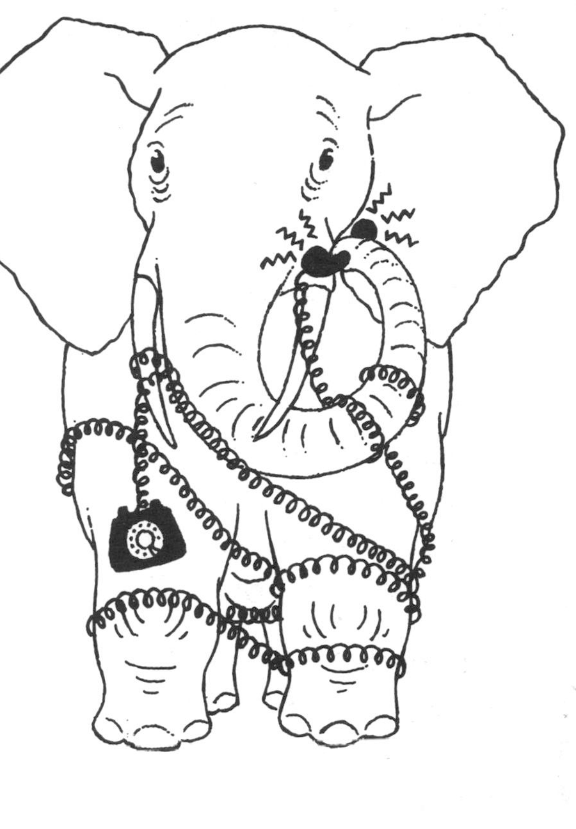

My dream pet

My sister keeps her tortoise
In a box beneath the sink.
Last night I shouted 'Heel!' to it,
But all it did was blink.

My brother has a goldfish,
It's a very silly pet —
Last night I tried to stroke it
And ended up all wet.

I dreamt I had a puppy,
And what we did all day
Was run and jump and hop and skip
And play and play and play!

Sandra Bell

Maria's party

Maria has a friend who is a spider —
She keeps it in her satchel in a box,
Maria has a friend who is a beetle —
It scuttles in a drawer behind her socks,
Maria has a friend who is a grass snake —
It slithers in a suitcase in the shed,
Maria has a friend who is a big grey slug —
She hides it in a jar beneath her bed.
Last week Maria asked her mother sweetly:
'Next Friday, can I have some friends to tea?'
Her mother said: 'Of course. Let's have a party.
I'll make some special cakes; we'll start at three.'

Maria's little friends enjoyed the party.
The beetle built a cave from crumbs of food,
The grass snake chased the spider through a trifle,
The slug sat on a scone and slowly chewed.
Yes, everyone enjoyed Maria's party,
A triumph, surely no one could deny,
Except, perhaps, Maria's missing mother —
She's still locked in the toilet . . .wonder why?

Richard Edwards

A teddy bear is soft and warm

A teddy bear is soft and warm,
You can cuddle him in bed,
A puppy dog is cute and likes
To be stroked upon his head.
A kitten has fur as soft as silk
And a gerbil is just as fine.
I love my pet, but I don't know yet
How to cuddle my porcupine.

Finola Akister

Beware!

The crocodile is coming!
It's heading for the pool,
It's swaying down the road
From the local Primary School.
Better keep your distance,
Better close your doors —
Beware the fearful clamour
From its ever-open jaws!
Be careful not to stumble
As you hurry from the street:
Remember that the crocodile
Has sixty tramping feet!
Through the city jungle
The creature marches on.
Wisely, shoppers stand aside
And wait until he's gone.
It's going to cross the busy street —
It starts to leave the path —
Attacked by snarling traffic
It's completely cut in half —
The head continues on its way,
The tail, delayed, just laughs
And runs to catch it up
At the Municipal Baths.
The crocodile is swimming
In the Public Swimming Pool,
But soon it will be heading
For the local Primary School.
So, better keep your distance,
Better if you try
To find a place to hide
While the crocodile goes by!

June Crebbin

The Jungle Sale

Once, before I went to school,
When I was only four,
I went to the village Jungle Sale
With Mary from next door.

The hall was full of people,
But, as far as I could see,
No sign of a lion or tiger,
Not a single chimpanzee.

And where were the
man-eating spiders?
Gorillas? Cockatoos?
Mary said that she'd buy me
A present —
but what could I choose?

There were piles of clothes
on the tables
That stood around the hall,
But no sign at all of an elephant
On the white elephant stall.

Still, I did go home with a
monkey
With wrap-around arms and tail,
And whatever Mum says,
I've kept him —
He's definitely Not for Sale.

June Crebbin

The Owl and the Pussycat and others

The Owl and the Pussycat

The Owl and the pussycat went to
sea
In a beautiful pea-green boat,
They took some honey, and plenty of
money
Wrapped up in a five-pound note.
The owl looked up to the stars
above,
And sang to a small guitar,
'O lovely pussy, O pussy, my love,
What a beautiful pussy you are,
You are,
You are!
What a beautiful pussy you are!'

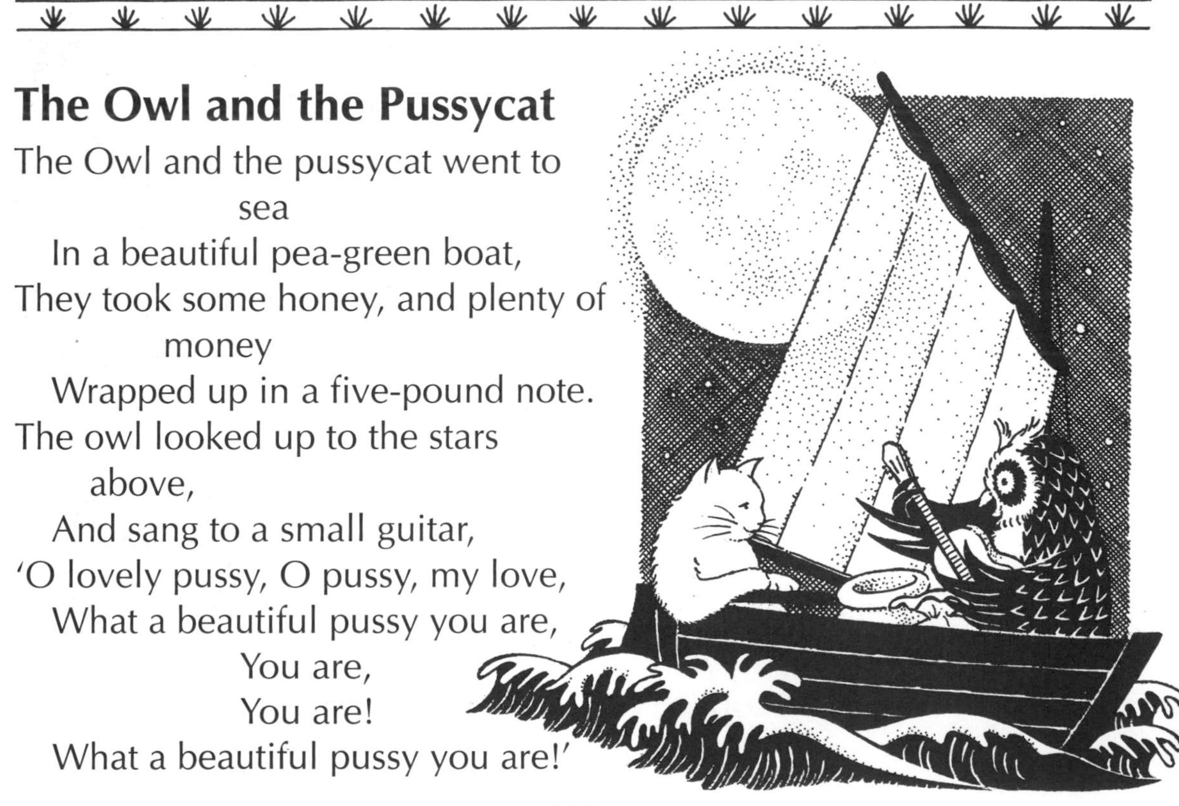

Pussy said to the owl, 'You elegant fowl,
How charmingly sweet you sing!
Oh! let us be married, too long we have tarried:
But what shall we do for a ring?'

They sailed away, for a year and a day,
To the land where the bong-tree grows;
And there in a wood a piggy-wig stood,
With a ring at the end of his nose.

'Dear pig, are you willing to sell for one shilling
Your ring?' Said the piggy, 'I will'.
So they took it away, and were married next day
By the Turkey who lives on the hill.
They dined on mince and slices of quince,
Which they ate with a runcible spoon;
And hand in hand, on the edge of the sand,
They danced by the light of the moon,
The moon,
The moon,
They danced by the light of the moon.

Edward Lear

A very wise bird

A very wise bird with a very long beak
Sat solemnly blinking away.
When asked why it was that he
never would speak,
He replied, 'I have nothing to say'.

Anon

Mister Owl

Mister owl, if you're so clever
Can you tell me why you never
Hunt by day when there's some light,
But try to catch your food at night?

Sandra Bell

My Rabbit

My rabbit's habit
Is jumping all about,
My rabbit's habit
Is trying to get out!

My rabbit's diet
Is lettuce leaves and such,
And my rabbit's
Habitat's
A little rabbit hutch!

Brenda Bradley

How to Tell a Tiger

People who know tigers
Very very well
All agree that tigers
Are not hard to tell.

The way to tell a tiger is
With lots of room to spare.
Don't try telling them up close
Or we may not find you there.

John Ciardi

Tiger To Tea

One day a tiger passing by
Came in at my garden gate.
He said to me
'May I come to tea
With a cup and a spoon and plate?'

I said 'Come in and be my guest
For I've just made a chocolate cake.
You can sit down there
In the rocking chair,
And how many lumps do you take?'

He washed his paws and licked his lips
His fur was as smooth as silk.
Then he said that he
Didn't care for tea
And please could he have some milk?

This tiger was neither fierce nor wild
(And I ought to have mentioned before)
That in the end
It was just pretend
He was really - the cat next door!

Margaret Thomas

Mouse

A mouse -
there's a mouse
in our cupboard!
I heard
a peculiar
squeak,
and I'm trying
my hardest
to catch her -
I've tried
every day
for a week.
I *know*
that she's there,
for whoever
could leave
such a mess
on the floor?
And who
would have nibbled
a boot box?
(It hadn't
been nibbled
before).
There *must* be
a mouse
in our cupboard.
An elephant
would be
too tall,
and so would
a cow
or a camel.

A mouse
is so secret
and small
that how
in the world
could I trap her?
She might be
curled up
in a shoe
with her tail
fastened over
her whiskers.
If I find her -
O, what
shall I do?

Jean Kenward

I am a mouse

I am a mouse.
With my beady black eyes
I can't see very well
So I can't always tell
When someone creeps near.

I am a mouse.
My sharp ears can hear
The scrape of a paw
Stealing over the floor.

I am a mouse.
I've a good sense of smell
If I sniff I can tell
When food's been left out
Or there's danger about.

I am a mouse.
When I'm frightened I race
For my hiding place.
In zig-zags I bound
Till I crawl safe and sound
Through the hole in the wall
Where I rest
In my nest.

John Foster

Last night I dreamed of chickens

Last night I dreamed of chickens,
there were chickens everywhere,
they were standing on my stomach,
they were nesting in my hair,
they were pecking at my pillow,
they were hopping on my head,
they were ruffling up their feathers
as they raced about my bed.
They were on the chairs and tables,
they were on the chandeliers,
they were roosting in the corners,
they were clucking in my ears,
there were chickens, chickens, chickens
for as far as I could see ...
when I woke today, I noticed
there were eggs on top of me.

Jack Prelutsky

Snail

A snail went by my window
With his shell-house on his back;
And as he wriggled down the path
He left a silvery track.

I think that snail is lucky
For if he has a fright
His house is right beside him
And he pops in out of sight.

Mary Dawson

My fish can ride a bicycle

My fish can ride a bicycle,
my fish can climb a tree,
my fish enjoys a glass of milk,
my fish takes naps with me.
My fish can play the clarinet,
my fish can bounce a ball,
my fish is not like other fish,
my fish can't swim at all.

Jack Prelutsky

The dragon-diner

I'm a twentieth century dragon,
I run the dragon-diner.
If it's fast food that you want,
You won't find any finer.

With a flick of the flame
From my fiery lips
I can sizzle you up
A steak and chips.

Beefburgers, bacon,
Crisp, crunchy fish,
Sausages, ham and eggs,
Name your dish!
I'm faster than a microwave.
There's no food finer.
If it's fast-food that you want,
Come to the dragon-diner.

John Foster

Elephants

If a hundred elephants
tried to board a bus
would the driver
make a fuss?

And if fifty elephants
came all together
to do their shopping at Tesco
would it cause
a fiasco?

And if twenty elephants
came to school
one morning
with books in their trunks,
would the teacher
keep her cool?

And if one
very little elephant,
smaller than all the rest
wanted to be my friend
for just one day,
would my mum
let him stay?

Irene Rawnsley

Acknowledgements

Acknowledgement is due to the following, whose permission is required for multiple reproduction:

ALLAN AHLBERG for his poem 'Haircut'; CAREY BLYTON for his poems 'Night starvation of the bitter bit' and 'Sing a song of science'; FELICITY BRYAN for the poems 'If I had shiny scissors' and 'If I could be a pilot' by Richard Edwards; LAURA CECIL for the poem 'Beech leaves' by James Reeves; STANLEY COOK for his poem 'In the playground'; JOHN C DESMOND for his poems 'Soft spot' and 'Song'; AILEEN FISHER for her poems 'Noses' and 'The furry ones'; ROBERT FROMAN for his poem 'Friendly warning'; TREVOR HARVEY for his poem 'Warmest greetings'; DAVID HIGHAM ASSOCIATES LTD for the poems 'The children's carol' and 'New clothes and old' by Eleanor Farjeon; DAVID HIGHAM ASSOCIATES LTD for the poem 'Mirror friends' by Jamila Gavin JOHN JOHNSON (AUTHOR'S AGENT) LTD for the poem 'Just when' by Max Fatchen; ROGER KEEN for the poem 'Giant' by Ivy O Eastwick; JEAN KENWARD for her poems 'At Christmas', 'The Crane', 'Giant Thunderclogs', 'Growing', 'Helicopter', 'Johnny', 'Seven old ladies', 'Shapes', 'Tears' and 'Why?'; HERBERT KRETZMER for his poem 'Yakkity yak'; ELIZABETH LINDSAY for her poem 'I swing'; DAPHNE LISTER for her poems 'A giant's so big', 'I've been growing', 'Large and small', 'Stripey tiger' and 'The kites'; WES MAGEE for his poem 'Climb the mountain'; JUDITH NICHOLLS for her poems 'Haircut', 'What's in the parcel?' and 'Who can tell?'; OCTOPUS CHILDREN'S PUBLISHING for the poem 'Furry bear' by A A Milne; PENGUIN BOOKS for the poems 'The octopus', 'The teddy bear' and 'The walrus' by Finola Akister; PENGUIN BOOKS for the poem 'If I wasn't me' by Allan Ahlberg; PETERS, FRASER & DUNLOP LTD for the poems 'A catterpillow' and 'Ever see a shark?' by Roger McGough; LAURENCE POLLINGER LTD for the poem 'The tip and the top' by Charlotte Zolotow; IRENE RAWNSLEY for her poem 'The giant visitor'; REED INTERNATIONAL BOOKS LTD for the poems 'Building a skyscraper' and 'Fourth floor' by James S Tippett; MARIAN REINER for the poem 'Said a long crocodile' by Lilian Moore from 'See my lovely poison ivy' © 1975 by Lilian Moore. Used by permission of Marian Reiner for the author; CLIVE RICHE for his poem 'Hooray for hair!'; ELIZABETH ROACH for the poem 'Christmas' by Marchette Chute; CAROLINE SHELDON LITERARY AGENCY for the poem 'Don't call alligator long mouth ...' by John Agard; IAN SOUTER for his poems 'Friends' and 'Schools up'; MARGARET THOMAS for her poem 'Giant size'; MRS J M TOMPKINS for the poem 'Holly' by John Tompkins; DAVE WARD for his poem 'My friend Dee'; A P WATT LTD for the poem 'The American elk' by Dick King-Smith; IRENE YATES for her poem 'Giants'; MRS B D BARTLETT for the poem 'You never know' by Olive Dove; CHARLES CAUSLEY for his poems 'Family Albums' and 'There was an old woman'; SUE COWLING for her peom 'Late night caller' from *What is kamquat?* published by Faber and Faber Ltd; J M DENT & SONS LTD for the poem 'The pines' by Margaret Mahy from *The first Margaret Mahy storybook*; JOHN C DESMOND for his poems 'Imagination', 'On the beach', 'Phew!' and 'Who did it?; AILEEN FISHER for her poem 'After a bath'; JOHN FOSTER for his poems 'The Shadow man' and 'What's that?' from *Ghost poems* published by Oxford University Press (1990); DAVID HIGHAM ASSOCIATES LTD for the poems 'The roundabout' by Clive Sansom and 'Jazz-Man' by Eleanor Farjeon; JOHN JOHNSON (AUTHOR'S AGENT) LTD for the poems 'Who?', 'The song of a mole', 'A forest by night' and 'Badgers' by Richard Edwards; JEAN KENWARD for her poems 'Goblin', 'The foal' and 'In the woods'; JAMES KIRKUP for his poem 'There was an old man' from *A first book of poetry* published by Oxford University Press; THE LITERARY TRUSTEES OF WALTER DE LA MARE and THE SOCIETY OF AUTHORS as their representative for the poem 'Someone' by Walter de la Mare; BRIAN MOSES for his poems 'Bouncy castle', 'Goodnight', 'Today was really hot' and 'Snow!'; JUDITH NICHOLLS for her poem 'Sack race'; PENGUIN BOOKS LTD for the poems 'Sore throat', 'There was a baby kangeroo' and 'Mary had a little lamb' by Finola Akister from *Before you go to bed* published by Puffin (1989); THE PETERS FRASER AND DUNLOP GROUP for the poem 'The sound collector' by Roger McGough; JOAN POULSON for her poems 'Like Grandad' and 'Aunty Betty'; IRENE RAWNSLEY for her poems 'The caterpillar fair' and 'Midnight visitors'; JOYCE RICHE for the poem 'Balloon' by Clive Riche; HELEN RUSSELL for her poem 'I'm really quite glad'; IAN SOUTER for his poem 'You don't frighten me!'; SPIKE MILLIGAN PRODUCTIONS for the poems 'My sister Laura' and 'Music makers' by Spike Milligan; IRENE YATES for her poems 'Watch out!', 'Being alone' and 'Great Grandad'; MOIRA ANDREW for her poem 'Shower'; MRS B D BARTLETT for the poems 'Octopus' and 'Who spoke?' by Olive Dove; MR A R BEAL for the poem 'The three unlucky men' by James Reeves; SANDRA BELL for her poem 'My dream pet'; FELICITY BRYAN for the poems 'Maria's party' and 'Tall Paul' by Richard Edwards; CENTURY HUTCHINSON LTD for the poem 'To a fat lady seen from the train' by Frances Cornford; ROBERT A CLARK for the poems 'Good Company' and 'Paddling' by Leonard Clark; SUE COWLING for her poem 'Houses'; JOHN C DESMOND for his poem 'Arthur Albert Algernon'; DEWES SKETCHLEY (SOLICITORS) for the poem 'Who's in' by Elizabeth Fleming; DOUBLEDAY (PUBLISHERS) for the poem 'Only in my opinion' by Monica Shannon; JOHN FOSTER for his poem 'Sand'; DAVID HIGHAM ASSOCIATES LTD for the poems 'The child in the train' and 'Waking up' by Eleanor Farjeon; DAVID HIGHAM ASSOCIATES LTD for the poem 'The radio men' by Elizabeth Jennings; JOHN JOHNSON (AUTHOR'S AGENT) LTD for the poems 'Littlemouse', 'Sunlight or surprise?' and 'Tears on Monday' by Richard Edwards; JEAN KENWARD for her poems 'Everything's wet', 'Grandpa Tortoise', 'Seaside', 'The alarm', 'Man in the Moon' and 'The snake'; PROFESSOR JAMES KIRKUP for his poem 'Scarecrow independence'; JOHN KITCHING for his poem 'Slugs'; DAPHNE LISTER for her poems 'A tale of woe!' and 'The sea's treasures'; ROGERS, COLERIDGE AND WHITE for 'The Quarrel', 'Waiting' and 'Wet' from *Orange Paw Marks* by Michelle Majorian; WES MAGEE for his poem 'Classroom circle of friends'; BRIAN MOSES for his poem 'Jellyfish'; OBERON PRESS for the poem 'Waiting for the first drop' from the collected poems of Raymond Souster; PENGUIN BOOKS LTD for the poem 'A teddy bear is soft and warm' by Finola Akister; THE PETERS, FRASER AND DUNLOP GROUP for the poem 'Intruders' by Roger McGough; IRENE RAWNSLEY for her poems 'Night train' and 'The animal picture book'; MARIAN REINER for the poem 'Until I saw the sea' by Lilian Moore from *I feel the same way* by Lilian Moore. Copyright © 1967 by Lilian Moore; ROGERS, COLERIDGE AND WHITE LTD for the poem 'What a wonderful day' by Tony Bradman; ROGERS, COLERIDGE AND WHITE LTD for the poem 'Sunday morning' by Brian Morse; IAN SOUTER for his poem 'Yesterday our family visited the seashore!'; MARGARET THOMAS for her poem 'Greedy gulls'; VIKING CHILDREN'S BOOKS for the poems 'Beware!' and 'The Jungle Sale' by June Crebbin from *The Jungle Sale* by June Crebbin (Viking Kestrel, 1988). Copyright © June Crebbin, 1988; A M WALSH for the poem 'Waving at trains' by John Walsh; COLIN WEST for his poem 'My uncle's umbrella'; IRENE YATES for her poems 'Can you guess?' and 'Inside'; IRENE RAWNSLEY for the poem 'Elephants'; JOHN L FOSTER for his poems 'I am a mouse' and 'The Dragon Diner'; JEAN KENWARD for the poems 'Mouse' and 'Winter Owl'; MARGARET THOMAS for the poem 'Tiger to tea'; BRENDA BRADLEY for the poem 'My Rabbit'; MARY DAWSON for the poem 'Snail'; WILLIAM MORROW & CO for 'Somersaults' by Jack Prelutsky from *Rainy Rainy Saturday*; JACK PRELUTSKY for 'My Fish Can Ride A Bicycle' and 'Last Night I dreamed of Chickens' from *Something Big Has Been Here* published by Heinemann; THE PETERS, FRASER AND DUNLOP GROUP for 'Stufferation' by Adrian Mitchell (none of Adrian Mitchell's poems are to be used in connection with any examination whatever.

The Publishers have made every attempt to trace the copyright holders, but in cases where they may have failed would be pleased to make the necessary arrangements at the first opportunity.